El Centro Campus

BIOL 1406 COURSE MANUAL

Biology for Science Majors I

Written and Edited by Professors

Graham, Snavely, and Gordon

XanEdu
17177 Laurel Park Drive
Suite 233
Livonia, MI 48152
800-562-2147
www.xanedu.com

Table of Contents

This page left intentionally blank

EL CENTRO CAMPUS BIOL 1406 PBL
Laboratory Safety

Goals
1. Describe the format of the laboratory class.
2. List the steps necessary to prepare for lab activities.
3. Explain the purpose of a Global Harmonized System (GHS) label and a Safety Data Sheet (SDS).
4. Understand the hazards of a specific chemical based on its GHS pictogram.
5. Describe the safety rules each student must follow when performing experiments.
6. Sign the Safety Roster, in which you agree to follow all safety rules in lab.

Activity 1.1: Laboratory Format

The laboratory portion of this course is designed to demonstrate that the concepts learned in the lecture portion apply to the real world. Some exercises presented in the handouts will be completed in lecture, while hands-on exercises will be performed in lab. Therefore, you must always remember to bring your course manual to lecture in order to complete necessary exercises.

- Exercises intended for the lecture section are marked with the following symbol:
    o You will not perform experiments involving chemicals or live organisms in lecture, but you will practice drawing important molecules and processes, as well as work with partners to solve biological riddles or problems.
    o These exercises must be completed and recorded in your handout or points will be deducted from your lecture grade.
    o When you successfully complete the exercises, you will better understand the concepts you will be applying later in lab.
    o Attendance in lecture is required to attend lab as many activities are started in lecture and completed in lab.

- Exercises performed in lab are marked with the following symbol:
    o These exercises allow you to learn about a concept in a practical fashion by conducting an experiment, performing a chemical test, or examining a biological specimen.
    o You will also need to complete all the lab exercises in the handout and answer post-lab questions in the back of the handout. Your instructor may deduct points from your daily lab quizzes if all lab exercises are not completed.
    o In addition, you will need the results of lab exercises to study for lab quizzes and projects.
    o All the checkpoints in your lab must be signed by your instructor before leaving.

Exercise 1.1a: Importance of Lecture   *Lecture*

If you miss a lecture class, what will the consequences be?

Exercise 1.1b: Importance of Lab   *Lecture*

If you miss a lab class, what will the consequences be?

Activity 1.2: Laboratory Safety

Laboratory classes allow students to participate in the field of biology and learn about the wonders of living organisms by conducting experiments. This hands-on approach will help you better understand concepts from the lecture portion of class. However, in order to properly perform the experiments, you must prepare in advance as well as follow important safety procedures for each laboratory exercise.

Preparing for Lab

- ➢ Students who read the lab exercises <u>prior</u> to attending lab will benefit the most.
  - You will work more efficiently and be more productive compared to those who did not prepare for the lab. Complete the Pre-Lab questions on the last page of the handout to check your understanding.
- ➢ Ask questions <u>before</u> starting your experiments.
  - Clear up any uncertainty with your instructor before mixing those vials, or you will waste time repeating the exercise.
- ➢ Clean your work area.
  - Use disinfectant and a paper towel to clean your table before you sit down.
- ➢ Clear your work area by stowing personal items under lab tables.
  - Backpacks, books, cell phones, jackets, and coats can be ruined and samples can be contaminated during an experiment.
- ➢ Know how to access the Safety Data Sheets (SDS or MSDS) for chemicals you use in lab.
  - SDS's contain specific information about hazards for each chemical used in the laboratory. They also specify what type of personal protection equipment should be used with a chemical. A notebook containing the SDS's is located in the laboratory prep room. Students should ask the instructor if they would like to review the SDS for chemicals used during labs.
- ➢ Recognize the symbol for biohazards and know where to discard them.
  - A biohazard is any part of an organism that could pose a threat to human health and must be discarded in special containers that are identified by the symbol to the right. There are several containers located throughout the lab.

- ➢ Know how to read the images from the Global Harmonized System (GHS) of Classification and Labeling of Chemicals.
  - These pictograms were adopted in 2003 by the United Nations as an international approach to hazard identification and communication. The GHS system of labels identifies the characteristics of chemicals using nine individual images.

The main elements of the GHS classification include physical, health, and environmental hazards. For example, a pictogram with flames indicates the substance is flammable and precautions should be taken to avoid heat when using or storing the substance. A pictogram of a skull and crossbones indicates the substance has the potential to be toxic and should not be handled without the proper personal protective equipment. When hazardous chemicals are used in lab, the lab handout will contain important information on the proper use of the chemical. To find out more information about any chemical used in lab, please ask to see a copy of the SDS.

The diagram below explains the different GHS ratings for each type of hazard.

Figure 1.1. GHS Pictograms and Explanations

Retrieved from: The University of Sydney, http://sydney.edu.au/science/chemistry/local-safety/5-1-introduction.shtml, 6/12/18.

Exercise 1.2a: Determining Hazards

Examine the GHS labels of the unknown chemicals at your workstation. What precautions would you take with each of these chemicals and what would you avoid while using them?

LABORATORY SAFETY RULES

1. Arrive on time and be attentive when instructions are given for the day's lab exercise.
2. Wear only closed-toe shoes in lab.
3. Keep your work station clean and organized.
4. Know where to find emergency equipment such as the eyewash, fire extinguisher, fire blanket, and telephone.
5. Do not eat or drink in lab. Repeat offenders will receive deductions from their quizzes.
6. Wear the recommended safety equipment when working with chemicals.
7. Report all accidents to your instructor immediately. Do not attempt to clean up blood-contaminated spills yourself.
8. Use extreme caution when working around hot plates and open flames. Do not leave heat sources unattended.
9. If chemicals come in contact with your skin or eyes, immediately flush with water for several minutes or use the eyewash and inform your lab instructor.
10. Always dispose of chemicals per lab instructor's directions. Many chemicals must be placed in a disposal container. **NEVER** return unused chemicals to their original containers.
11. Dispose of biological hazard materials in the biohazard containers.
12. Dispose of broken glassware in glass disposal box.
13. Do not use equipment without instruction.
14. Clean all glassware with soap and water and return them to their original location.
15. Your workstation and other areas utilized must be clean before the end of class. Offenders may receive deductions from their quizzes.

 Exercise 1.2b: Signing the Safety Roster

Before leaving lab today, you are required to watch the safety video and sign the safety roster. By signing the safety roster, you agree to follow all safety rules and other instructions given by your instructor. You will not be allowed to participate in any lab exercises if you fail to sign the roster.

Checkpoint A

BIOL 1406 - Laboratory Safety Questions

Pre-Lab Questions

1. You cannot eat or drink in lab.
   a. True
   b. False

2. When do you need to clean your table?
   a. Before class starts
   b. After you finish your lab
   c. Both before and after
   d. Never

3. What GHS pictogram indicates a skin irritant?

   _____

4. What document would you read to find out detailed hazards about a chemical?

   _____

5. To fully prepare, students should read the handout before class.
   a. True
   b. False

6. You should do the Pre-Lab questions before lab and the Post-Lab questions after lab.
   a. True
   b. False

Post-Lab Questions

1. Look at your schedule to find out what you will be doing for your next lab. What should you do to prepare for the next class?

2. What would be an example of a biohazard and how would you need to dispose of it?

3. Maria examines the labels on a chemical bottle and sees the following. What safety precautions should Maria take when using this chemical?

4. Explain the hazards of eating or drinking in the laboratory, wearing open-toed shoes, and disposing of glass in the trash.

5. Bob is conducting an experiment and must use several hazardous chemicals. While pouring out a powdered chemical, Bob gets some into his eyes. It stings only for a few seconds so Bob finishes the experiment, cleans up, and leaves. Bob is rushed to the emergency room a few hours later. What are the laboratory safety rules Bob violated?

Goals
1. Identify the steps of the scientific method.
2. Identify units of measurement used in science.
3. Convert between metric units.
4. Measure length, mass, volume, and temperature using the metric system.
5. Collect and analyze data using the scientific method.

Activity 2.1: The Scientific Method

Researchers throughout the world use a standardized technique of answering scientific questions. This technique is called the **scientific method**. You will use the scientific method throughout this course to critically investigate your environment.

There are typically seven steps to the scientific method:

1. **Observation**
   - As you investigate your environment, you will observe many interesting phenomena.

2. **Question**
   - You will immediately begin to ask questions about what you observe.

3. **Hypothesis**
   - Your question can be turned into a hypothesis, which is an educated, yet untested **answer** to the question.
   - Your hypothesis must be testable and falsifiable. This means we must be able to design an experiment to test the validity of your hypothesis. If your hypothesis is not true, your results should reject your hypothesis.

4. **Prediction**
   - If you test your hypothesis by conducting an experiment, what should your results be?

5. **Experiment**
   - To test your hypothesis, you must design an experiment. An experiment attempts to support or disprove a hypothesis.
   - One mistake can ruin your results. To ensure your results are correct, be careful when collecting data from your experiment.

6. **Analysis**
   - You will need to closely examine data you collect to interpret the results of the experiment. You may have to perform your experiment multiple times to increase your certainty of the results.

7. **Conclusion**
   - After analysis of your data, can you support or reject your hypothesis? No results can prove a hypothesis.
   - If the results of your experiment neither supports nor rejects your hypothesis, you may need to modify your hypothesis for future experiments.

Match the descriptions (A-G) to the correct step of the scientific method:

1. _____ Observation

2. _____ Question

3. _____ Hypothesis

4. _____ Prediction

5. _____ Experiment

6. _____ Analysis

7. _____ Conclusion

A. The results support Miranda's explanation – sugar does dissolve more readily in hot tea.

B. While making iced tea, Miranda notices that when she adds sugar and stirs, most of it does not dissolve – it settles to the bottom of the pitcher.

C. Miranda anticipates that if she adds the sugar to the tea when it is hot, then the sugar will dissolve better than using cold tea, as the ability of sugar to dissolve may depend upon the temperature of the tea.

D. Miranda wonders, "Can I do something to make more sugar dissolve?" She knows that sugar seems to dissolve quickly in her hot coffee – would it be the same for tea?

E. No undissolved sugar can be seen at the bottom of the first cup. A small amount of sugar can be seen at the bottom of the second cup. A larger amount of sugar can be seen at the bottom of the third cup.

F. Miranda thinks about it and comes up with an answer – using hot tea will cause the sugar to dissolve more readily.

G. Miranda makes three cups of tea in clear cups and adds two tablespoons of sugar when the cups are at different temperatures. For the first cup, she adds the sugar while the tea is still very hot. The second she lets cool to room temperature before she adds the sugar. The third she puts in the refrigerator for 5 minutes before adding the sugar.

Activity 2.2: Measuring for Science

When we make observations or perform experiments to test a hypothesis in science, the information we collect is often recorded as a measurement. To ensure consistency, scientists around the world use the same measurement standard, the **metric system**. The metric system is based on units of ten, which simplifies conversion from one metric unit to another. In the metric system, length is measured in meters (m), mass is measured in grams (g), and volume is measured in liters (L).

When measuring, it is important to remember two concepts: accuracy and precision. **Accuracy** is how close a measured value is to the actual value, while **precision** is the ability of a measurement to be consistently reproduced.

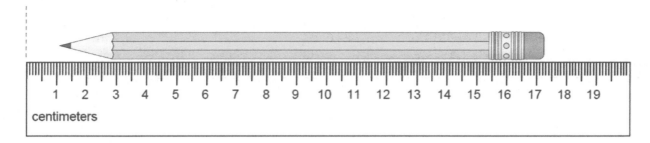

If you do not know how to properly use a ruler, you can measure a pencil five times and precisely obtain a measurement of 17.3 centimeters although the accurate length of the pencil is 16.2 centimeters. The proper use of measuring devices is essential for accuracy. But what about the measurement itself? Knowing a pencil is 16.2 centimeters means nothing if we do not know what a centimeter is.

A centimeter is a metric unit for length. The base unit of length in the metric system is the meter, which is a little over three feet, and the prefix *centi-* means a hundredth. Therefore, a centimeter is a hundredth of a meter, meaning we can fit one hundred centimeters into a meter. As the metric system is based on units of ten, conversion from one metric unit to another is relatively easy. Table 2.1 shows the prefixes for various powers of ten used in the metric system.

Table 2.1. Prefixes in the metric system:

Prefix	Symbol	Meaning	Exponential Form
Giga	G	1,000,000,000	10^9
Mega	M	1,000,000	10^6
Kilo	k	1,000	10^3
Hecta	h	100	10^2
Deca	da	10	10^1
Base unit		1	10^0
Deci	d	0.1	10^{-1}
Centi	c	0.01	10^{-2}
Milli	m	0.001	10^{-3}
Micro	μ	0.000001	10^{-6}
Nano	n	0.000000001	10^{-9}

Basic units of the metric system:
- ➤ Length is measured in **meters** (m)
- ➤ Mass is measured in **grams** (g)
- ➤ Volume is measured in **liters** (L)
- ❖ Temperature in this lab will be measured in **degrees Celsius** (°C), which is not a metric unit

Exercise 2.2a: Chart of Measurements   *Lecture*

Use Table 2.1 to help you complete the chart.

Measurement (without unit)	Type of Measurement	Symbol	Exponential Form of Prefix	Conversion to Basic Units*
10	Length	10 cm	10^{-2}	0.1 m
5	Mass		10^3	
		100 mL		
55000000		55000000 µg		
42	Length		10^{-3}	
		.0054 km		
500	Volume		10^0	

The basic units in the last column are mentioned on the previous page: meter, liter, and gram.

Activity 2.3: Time to Measure!

Now that you know what items you want to measure, how are you going to take the measurements? Do you know how to properly use a ruler, electronic scale, graduated cylinder, pipette, and thermometer? You must know how to use the measuring equipment to measure accurately. If you measure from the wrong spot on the ruler or look at the wrong line on a graduated cylinder, you will not get the correct measurement. Precision is also important, so it is important to measure multiple times to ensure you are consistently obtaining the same measurement

 Exercise 2.3a: Examination of Meter stick and Ruler

Materials needed: meter stick, ruler

Identify which section of the ruler has metric units (centimeters) and which has standard units (inches).

- What is the smallest unit you can measure with the ruler?

- How many millimeters are in a centimeter?

- How many centimeters are in a meter?

 Exercise 2.3b: Collect Data for Length Practice

Use the meter stick or ruler to measure the length of at least three items. Measure one item using meters, one item using centimeters, and another item using milimeters. Have another team member also measure the same item(s) to make sure your measurements are accurate and precise.

Item	Measurement #1	Measurement #2	Do measurements agree?
1.			
2.			
3.			

 Exercise 2.3c: Collect Data for Area Practice

To determine area, measure the width and length of an item, then multiply the two measurements.
- What should you do to the units to show width and length have been multiplied?

Use the ruler to measure the area of at least one item. Have another team member also measure the same item to make sure your measurements are accurate and precise.

Item	Measurement #1	Measurement #2	Do measurements agree?
4.			

 Exercise 2.3d: Collect Data for Volume Practice

Materials needed: 100 mL beaker, 50 mL graduated cylinder

Volume is a three-dimensional measurement of how much space an object occupies. Fill a beaker with water and pour 20 mL of water into a 50 mL gradated cylinder. Note that the top of the water column is curved – this is known as the **meniscus**. Use the bottom of the meniscus when measuring volume.

- To correctly <u>read</u> the volume, are your eyes above, below or level with the meniscus?

Using the beaker, measure 50mL of water. Now pour this volume of water into the graduated cylinder. What is the volume according to the graduated cylinder? Record your results in the table.

Item	Measurement #1 (Beaker)	Measurement #2 (Grad. cylinder)	Do measurements agree?
5.			

- Does a beaker or the graduated cylinder more accurately measure volume? Why?

Exercise 2.3e: Collect Data for Mass Practice

Materials needed: electronic scale, weigh boats

Mass is a two-dimensional measurement of the amount of matter an object contains. If you measure an object that needs a container (like water or powder), you must eliminate the mass of the container. You do this by **"taring"** the scale. After placing the container on the scale, press the On-Zero Off/Tare button briefly and this will reset the scale to zero. The "snowflake" that shows up in the lower left corner of the scale indicates that the mass is stable. You may then add the sample to the container.

Use the scale to measure the mass of at least two items. Have another team member also measure the same item to make sure your measurements are accurate and precise.

- The scale should be measuring mass with metric units. Is it?

Item	Measurement #1	Measurement #2	Do measurements agree?
6.			
7.			

 Exercise 2.3f: Collect Data for Temperature Practice

Materials needed: ice, beakers, thermometers on side table

Temperature measures the degree of heat an object has and while there are different units that scientists use to measure temperature, we will use degrees Celsius (°C) in this class. For the Celsius scale, water freezes at 0°C and boils at 100°C.

Use the thermometer to measure the temperature of at least two items. Have another team member also measure the same item to make sure your measurements are accurate and precise.

Item	Measurement #1	Measurement #2	Do measurements agree?
8.			
9.			

Checkpoint A

Pre-Lab Questions

1. Which is the largest unit of measurement?
   a. Millimeter
   b. Micrometer
   c. Kilometer

2. A kilometer is _____ meters, while a millimeter is a _____ of a meter.

3. Water freezes at _____ °C and boils at _____ °C.

4. If you measured the amount of space the water in a glass occupied, what would you be measuring?
   a. Length
   b. Volume
   c. Mass

5. What is a possible explanation of a scientific problem?

   _____

Post-Lab Questions

1. What do the prefixes milli-, centi-, and kilo mean? Use an example to explain how they differ from one another.

2. You need to measure the mass and length of a pencil. How would you do this and what units would you use?

3. If water boils at 100°C, what is the approximate temperature of a hot summer day in Dallas in degrees Celsius? Explain your answer.

4. Why is the scientific method necessary when performing experiments? To help explain, describe the problems a scientist might encounter if he/she did not utilize the scientific method to answer a scientific question.

5. How does a hypothesis differ from a question? Use an example in your answer.

6. What are beakers, graduated cylinders, and pipets used to measure? What specific unit did you use in all of your measurements using this equipment? What is the digital scale used to measure? What units did you use when using the scale? What are rulers and meter sticks used to measure? What units did you use when using the rulers and meter stick?

Goals
1. Define atom, proton, electron, neutron, element, compound, and molecule.
2. Draw the atomic structure of biologically important elements.
3. Use the periodic table to determine the characteristics of elements.
4. Distinguish between ionic, covalent polar and covalent nonpolar bonds.
5. Understand chemical formulas and investigate chemical reactions.

Activity 3.1: Elements and Atoms

At the most basic level, life is composed of chemicals. Therefore, the study of life must include the study of chemistry, which focuses on the structure and properties of matter. The **atom** is the basic unit of matter and consists of three different stable subatomic particles: protons, neutrons and electrons. Negatively charged **electrons** orbit the nucleus, which contains positively charged **protons** and neutral **neutrons**. In neutral atoms (those without a positive or negative charge) the number of protons equals the number of electrons.

Electrons occupy certain shells around the nucleus based on their energy levels. The lowest energy electrons are found in the first shell, which is closest to the nucleus. The first shell can hold a maximum of two electrons. Subsequent shells carry electrons with higher energy levels and these shells can hold a maximum of eight electrons. For example, neutral atoms of the element carbon have six protons and six electrons, so two shells are found surrounding the nucleus. Two of the six electrons are found in the first shell, while the remaining four electrons are in the second shell. The configuration of electrons for a carbon atom is diagrammed in Figure 3.1.

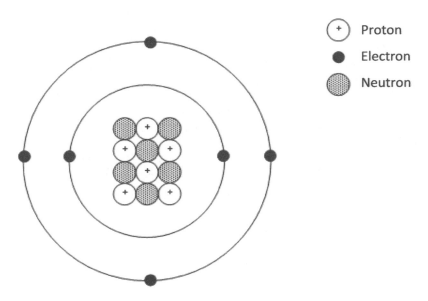

Figure 3.1. Atomic Structure of a Carbon Atom

A substance consisting of one type of atom is referred to as an **element** and can be distinguished by its **atomic number**, which is the number of *protons* in its nucleus. Table 3.1 lists some of the elements you will become familiar with while studying the chemistry of life.

Table 3.1. Common Elements in Biology

Element	Symbol	Atomic Number
Hydrogen	H	1
Carbon	C	6
Nitrogen	N	7
Oxygen	O	8
Sodium	Na	11
Magnesium	Mg	12
Phosphorus	P	15
Sulfur	S	16
Chlorine	Cl	17
Potassium	K	19
Calcium	Ca	20
Iron	Fe	26

Exercise 3.1a: Drawing Atomic Structure   *Lecture*

Based on the atomic number in Table 3.1 and assuming an <u>equal number of protons and electrons</u> in each atom, draw the atomic structure of the following elements.

Hydrogen   Carbon   Nitrogen

Oxygen   Sodium   Chlorine

Activity 3.2: The Periodic Table

The **periodic table** of elements lists all the chemical elements known to science. Each element is assigned a specific symbol and is arranged according to its **atomic number**, which equals the number of protons in that element. The elements in the same column have similar characteristics because they have a similar number of electrons in their outermost electron shell (valence shell). Although the number of protons in atoms of the same element cannot vary, the number of neutrons found in each atom can vary, resulting in **isotopes**. Isotopes of the same element react identically but are distinguishable by their mass number. The **mass number** of each isotope equals the sum of protons and neutrons; averaging an element's isotopes based on the percentages found in nature results in the average **atomic mass** on the periodic table. For example: The element carbon has three isotopes based on neutron number: Carbon-12 (also written ^{12}C) has 6 neutrons and a mass number of 12, Carbon-13 (^{13}C) has 7 neutrons and a mass number of 13, and Carbon-14 (^{14}C) has 8 neutrons and a mass number of 14. The natural abundances of carbon isotopes are 98.9% for ^{12}C, 1.1% for ^{13}C, and only a trace for ^{14}C. Therefore, the average atomic mass equals 12.01.

✏️ **Exercise 3.2a: Examining Specific Isotopes** *Lecture*

You will now use your chemistry knowledge to determine certain characteristics of specific isotopes. We'll first look at Magnesium in Table 3.2 as an example. We know from the Periodic Table that Magnesium has the chemical symbol of Mg and has an atomic number of 12, which means Mg has 12 protons. Notice in Table 3.2 that the mass number for this isotope is 25, which indicates that this isotope has 13 neutrons in its nucleus (25 – 12 = 13). This isotope of Mg also has 10 electrons. That means this isotope has two more protons than it does electrons. This is why the charge of this isotope is 2+ and why this isotope is also an **ion** (a charged atom). As you are considering specific isotopes, **complete Table 3.2 based upon the information given.** Use Table 3.1, not the Periodic Table for this activity.

Table 3.2. Properties of Different Isotopes

ID	Element	Symbol	Number of Protons	Number of Electrons	Number of Neutrons	Mass Number of Isotope	Charge of Isotope	Is This Isotope an Ion*?
Ex	Magnesium	Mg	12	10	13	25	2+	Yes
A	Oxygen			8		16		
B			7	7	7			
C		K				38	0	
D	Hydrogen		1		0		0	
E			6		7		0	
F	Sodium					23	1+	
G		Fe		24	30			
H			12		14		2+	
I	Chlorine				18		1-	
J		P		14		31		

Figure 3.2. The Periodic Table of Elements

Activity 3.3: Chemical Bonds and Molecules

Compounds consist of two or more elements bound together in order to fill their outer shells (called **valence shells**) to achieve stability. The 'noble gases' already possess full valence shells and can be found in the last column of the periodic table. Noble gases, such as neon, do not react with other elements to form bonds and are chemically inert. Atoms of all the other elements are unstable and <u>must</u> react with other atoms to obtain full valence shells. There are two types of strong chemical bonds: **ionic bonds** and **covalent bonds**.

Ionic bonds involve the loss or gain of electrons and the creation of **ions** (charged atoms). Elements that form ionic bonds have great differences of **electronegativity** (the affinity an atom has for electrons). Ionic bonds result in the formation of salts; sodium chloride (ordinary table salt) is one of the best known examples. A chlorine atom is very electronegative due to the seven electrons in its valence shell. On the other hand, a sodium atom has only one electron in its valence shell and has very low electronegativity. As chlorine needs only one additional electron to fill its valence shell, it seizes sodium's one valence electron. This results in stability for both chlorine and sodium, as both now have eight electrons in their outer shells. Due to the gain of an electron, chlorine takes on a negative charge and becomes a negatively-charged ion (**anion**); sodium loses an electron, takes on a positive charge, and becomes a positively-charged ion (**cation**). The opposite charges of the ions attract resulting in an ionic bond.

Atoms can also fill their valence shells by sharing electrons, resulting in the formation of strong **covalent** bonds. Two or more atoms held together by covalent bonds are referred to as **molecules**. A hydrogen atom does not exist on its own in nature, but two hydrogen atoms can achieve stability by forming a single covalent bond (forming molecular hydrogen, H_2). Each hydrogen atom has one valence electron, so both atoms fill their first shell by sharing the electrons. This is an example of a **nonpolar** covalent bond, because both atoms have the same electronegativity (affinity for the shared electrons). Molecular oxygen is similar, but the two oxygen molecules share four electrons, resulting in a double covalent bond. The covalent bonds found in a molecule of water, however, are **polar**. Water consists of an oxygen atom covalently bound to two hydrogen atoms. Because oxygen is more electronegative than hydrogen, it pulls the electrons slightly toward itself, producing a partial negative charge around the oxygen atom. The electrons do not spend as much time orbiting the hydrogen atoms, so the hydrogen atoms take on a partial positive charge. This unequal sharing of electrons is called a **polar** covalent bond because it produces a molecule that is <u>neutral overall</u>, but with <u>partial charges on opposite ends</u> (sometimes called "poles").

Each element has its own electronegativity value depending upon how many valence electrons it has. Electronegativity increases as the number of valence electrons increases. Thus, elements in the first column of the periodic table have low electronegativity, while elements in the seventeenth column have high electronegativity. The electronegativity values of some common biological elements are shown in Table 3.3.

Table 3.3. Electronegativities of Common Biological Elements

Element	Electronegativity Value
Hydrogen	2.1
Carbon	2.5
Nitrogen	3.0
Oxygen	3.5
Sodium	0.9
Chlorine	3.0

✎ **Exercise 3.3a: Electronegativity and Chemical Bonds**

Use Table 3.3 on the previous page to answer these questions.

- Which is the most electronegative element in Table 3.3? _____

- Which is the least electronegative element in Table 3.3? _____

The difference in electronegativity values is one factor that determines what types of bonds will form between two atoms: 0.4 or less = nonpolar covalent bond, greater than 0.4 but less than 1.7 = polar covalent bond, 1.7 or greater = ionic bond. For example, if a bond formed between two hydrogen atoms, it would be a nonpolar covalent bond since both atoms have electronegativity values of 2.1 and the difference between the values is zero (2.1 -2.1 = 0).

- Based on the information above, what type of bond will form between carbon and hydrogen?

- Based on the information above, what type of bond will form between sodium and chlorine?

- Based on the information above, what type of bond will form between oxygen and nitrogen?

🖐 **Exercise 3.3b. Draw the Atoms**

For this activity you will use the atom templates below to draw several of the most common elements found in biology. The grey portion of each atom represents the nucleus of each atom. The black rings around the outside of each represent the electron shells.

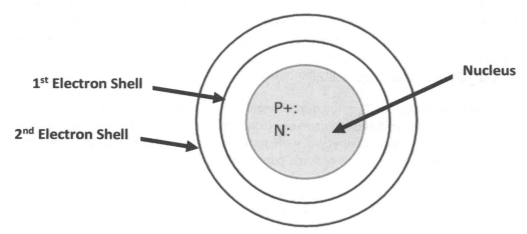

1. Examine the atom templates below. Given the number of electron shells shown for each, determine which template belongs to each of the following elements: Oxygen, Nitrogen, Hydrogen, Carbon, Sodium, and Chlorine. **_Check with your instructor before you move on!_**
2. Fill in the contents of the nucleus of each atom. How do you know how many protons there should be? What about the neutrons?
3. <u>Assuming all atoms as shown are neutral</u> draw in the appropriate number of electrons. How many should each electron shell hold?

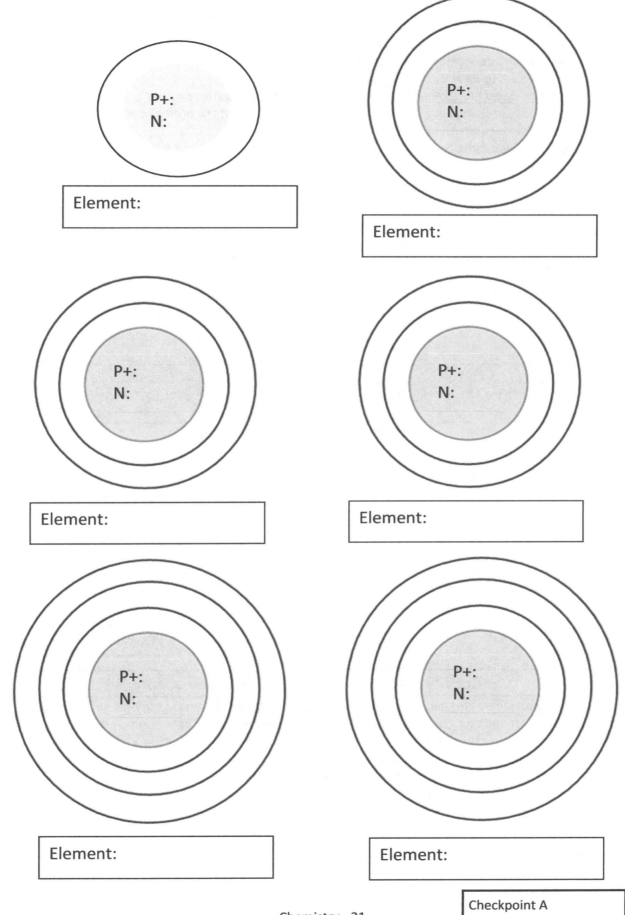

P+:
N:

Element:

P+:
N:

Element:

P+:
N:

Element:

P+:
N:

Element:

P+:
N:

Element:

P+:
N:

Element:

Checkpoint A

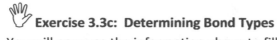 **Exercise 3.3c: Determining Bond Types**

You will now use the information above to fill out Table 3.4.

1. Use Table 3.3 to fill in the missing information in Table 3.4.
   a. For "Most Electronegative Atom?" use the electronegativity values to determine the atom with the strongest electronegativity in the molecule. *If the atoms have equivalent electronegativity*, write "Equal".
   b. Determine the type of bond that will form between the atoms based on the difference in the electronegativities of the two atoms.
   c. For "Charges?" answer "Full" for ionic compounds, "Partial" for polar molecules, and "None" for nonpolar molecules.

Table 3.4. Making molecules using common atoms

Molecule	Molecular Formula	Structural Formula	Most Electronegative Atom?	Bond type *	Charges?
Hydrogen	H_2	H—H			
Oxygen	O_2	O=O			
Methane	CH_4	H—C—H (with H above and H below C)			
Ammonia	NH_3	H—N—H (with H below N)			
Water	H_2O	O with H and H			
Sodium chloride	NaCl				

*0.4 or less = nonpolar covalent bond, greater than 0.4 but less than 1.7 = polar covalent bond, 1.7 or greater = ionic bond

- Why is there no structural formula provided for NaCl?

Checkpoint B

Activity 3.4: Chemical Formulas and Reactions

A **chemical formula** identifies each element in a compound by using chemical symbols. If a molecule contains more than one atom of a particular element, this quantity is indicated using a subscript after the chemical symbol. A **structural formula** shows the actual arrangement of atoms in a compound. For example, as shown in Table 3.5, molecular oxygen can be represented in two different ways. In the chemical formula the symbol for oxygen has a subscript of 2, indicating two oxygen atoms make up one molecule of oxygen. In the structural formula two oxygen symbols are bound together by two solid lines, each line representing a covalent bond. As you learned earlier, two electrons are shared in each one of these bonds.

Table 3.5. Formulas for Common Molecules

Molecule	Chemical Formula	Structural Formula
Oxygen	O_2	O=O
Hydrogen	H_2	H—H
Water	H_2O	O—H $\mid$ H

Chemical formulas are used in chemical equations to describe chemical reactions. A **chemical reaction** is when one substance is transformed into one or more different substances. The chemicals found in organisms are constantly reacting with one another. Let's examine the chemical reaction that occurs when you eat too much pizza and take an antacid to relieve your heartburn.

$$CaCO_3 + 2HCl \rightarrow CaCl_2 + H_2O + CO_2$$

Heartburn is caused by too much hydrochloric acid in your stomach, represented by the chemical formula HCl. The active ingredient of the antacid you take is calcium carbonate ($CaCO_3$). These two compounds are the **reactants** of the chemical equation. The arrow indicates a chemical reaction is occurring between the reactants. To the right of the arrow are the **products** of the reaction. When calcium carbonate reacts with hydrochloric acid, three products are created: calcium chloride ($CaCl_2$), water (H_2O), and carbon dioxide (CO_2). For a chemical formula to be balanced the number of atoms of each element must be equal on both sides of the arrow. Identify the three oxygen molecules on each side of the equation. Note the "2" in front of the hydrochloric acid (HCl). This is a **coefficient** that shows that 2 HCl compounds (2 H and 2 Cl) are involved in the reaction. When calcium carbonate chemically reacts with the hydrochloric acid three relatively harmless compounds are produced as a result.

✎ **Exercise 3.4a: Writing Reactions** *Lecture*

Sodium carbonate (Na_2CO_3) undergoes a chemical reaction to form sodium oxide (Na_2O) and carbon dioxide (CO_2). Write the chemical equation for this reaction.

Pre-Lab Questions

1. What makes up matter and cannot be broken down by physical/chemical means?

   _____

2. Which subatomic particle is negatively charged?
   a. Proton
   b. Electron
   c. Neutron

3. Na is the chemical symbol for

   _____.

4. Which are the two types of strong bonds?
   a. Covalent and ionic
   b. Ionic and hydrogen
   c. Hydrogen and covalent

5. What is the degree of the affinity an atom has for electrons called?

   _____

Post-Lab Questions

1. Describe the atomic structure of a magnesium atom (i.e. locations and amounts of protons, electrons, neutrons).

2. All of the elements in the first column of the periodic table are referred to as alkali metals because they have similar properties. What similarities do they share with regard to electrons?

3. You are on a game show and will win one million dollars if you can identify an atom. You are told the isotope has a mass number of 12 amu and it has four valence electrons. How will you solve this problem?

4. An ionic bond is formed when chlorine and potassium react with one another. Why do you suppose these elements do not share electrons in a covalent bond?

5. Explain why a water molecule is dipole, or has two different "poles".

6. What is wrong with the following chemical equation?

$$2 H_2 + O_2 \rightarrow 2 H_3O + N_2$$

EL CENTRO CAMPUS BIOL 1406 PBL
Solutions

Goals
1. Define and identify solution, solvent and solute.
2. Explain how functional groups affect the solubility of a molecule.
3. Define acids, bases, buffers, and the pH scale.
4. Test the pH of substances and determine if they are buffers.

Activity 4.1: Water

All life on Earth requires water to survive. Water contains one oxygen (O) atom and two hydrogen (H) atoms bound by covalent bonds. Despite sharing their electrons, water molecules are polar because the valence electrons are shared unequally between the oxygen and hydrogen atoms. Oxygen has a greater electronegativity than hydrogen, meaning it is highly attractive to electrons and pulls more strongly on the shared electrons, keeping them closer to itself. This unequal sharing of electrons means that the electrons cluster at the oxygen end of the molecule, leaving the hydrogen ends of the molecule partially positive and the oxygen end partially negative. Water's many unique properties are due to its polarity.

 Exercise 4.1a: Properties of Water   *Lecture*
- What are the properties of water?

 Exercise 4.1b: Demonstrate the Properties of Water

As a lab group, come up with various ways to show your instructor at least 5 properties of water. (Materials to use will be provided by your instructor or you can find items on your own.)
- How did you demonstrate these properties?

Checkpoint A

As the vast majority of living organisms are mostly composed of water, chemicals in living systems exist in an aqueous environment. In this dynamic medium some of those chemicals are reacting with one another, while others are not. When you put different atoms/molecules together, they do not always react to create new molecules. For example, when you combine salt (NaCl) and baking soda ($NaHCO_3$) together for baking, the molecules do not recombine to form a new product. This is an example of a **mixture**, a combination of two substances that retain their original structures. A **solution** is a specific type of mixture that consists of a liquid **solvent**, such as water, in which a **solute**, such as NaCl, is dissolved.

Exercise 4.2a: What is in a Solution?   *Lecture*

- Describe the composition of a glass of lemonade, using the concept of a solution.

Molecules contain groups of atoms that allow for greater or lesser solubility in water. **Functional groups** are usually chemically reactive and the types of functional groups an organic molecule contains determine its characteristics. Some of the most common functional groups are displayed in Table 4.1. The more polar (hydrophilic) the functional group, the greater its solubility in water.

Table 4.1. Common Functional Groups

Group	Structure	Example	
Hydroxyl	—OH	Ethanol	
Carbonyl	—CO—	Acetone	
Carboxyl	—COOH	Acetic Acid	
Amino	—NH₂	Methylamine	
Phosphate	—H₂PO₄	Glycerate 3-phosphate	
Sulfhydryl	—SH	Butanethiol	
Methyl	—CH₃	Ethane	

✎ **Exercise 4.2b: Determining Solubility**

- Which would be more soluble in water: ethanol or ethane? Why?

Activity 4.3: Acids, Bases and pH

In living organisms, chemicals are found in an aqueous (liquid) environment, which consists of water. Although water is a neutral substance, an extremely small amount of water molecules **dissociates**, or breaks apart, into charged ions: positive hydrogen ions (protons) and negative hydroxide ions. The protons combine with water molecules to form hydronium ions. This reaction is reversible and the ions can easily recombine to form water, as indicated by the double arrow.

$$2H_2O \leftrightarrow H_3O^+ + OH^-$$

When an **acid** is added to water, the concentration of hydrogen ions increases. For example, in water hydrochloric acid dissociates into hydrogen ions and chlorine ions.

$$HCl \rightarrow H^+ + Cl^-$$

A **base** is a substance that decreases the hydrogen ion concentration directly or by releasing hydroxide ions which combine with hydrogen ions to form water. For example, ammonia (NH_3) combines directly with hydrogen ions, while sodium hydroxide (NaOH) dissociates into sodium and hydroxide ions:

$$NH_3 + H^+ \rightarrow NH_4^+ \qquad\qquad NaOH \rightarrow Na^+ + OH^-$$

The pH scale is used to indicate the strength of acids and bases. The pH is a measure of the hydrogen ion concentration of a solution and ranges from 0 to 14. Pure water has a pH of 7, which means the hydrogen and hydroxide ions equal one another. Acids have a pH below 7 and the hydrogen ion concentration increases as the pH decreases toward 0. Bases have a pH above 7 and the hydrogen ion concentration decreases as the pH increases toward 14. The relative concentrations of hydrogen and hydroxide ions are shown in Figure 4.3 for the different pH values.

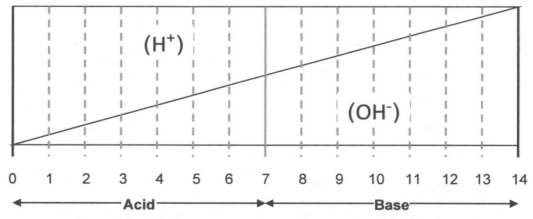

Figure 4.3. Relative concentrations of ions across the pH Scale

✎ **Exercise 4.3a: Acid or Base?**   *Lecture*

You will test the pH of HCl and NH_3. Which is the acid and which is the base? Why?

Exercise 4.3b: Testing pH

Materials needed: pH paper, paper towel, items to test, gloves, scissors, safety goggles

1. After putting on gloves and goggles, examine the items you will test.
2. For each item, make a prediction of its pH and write this in the table below.
3. Carefully cut off 2 cm long pieces of the pH paper and place on a paper towel.
4. Place a **SMALL** drop of each item on different pH papers and compare with the scale on the pH paper container.
5. Read the results within 10 seconds and write your results in the chart below.
6. Based on the actual pH, note whether it is neutral, acidic, or basic in the table.

Item	Predicted pH	Actual pH	Acid/Base/Neutral
Ammonia			
Lemon juice			
Mouthwash			
Vinegar			
HCl			
Unknown A			
Unknown B			
Unknown C			

- Which prediction differed the most from the actual pH? What did you base your prediction on and do you think any errors affected the results?

Checkpoint B

Activity 4.4: Acids, Bases and pH

Buffers are found in organisms to keep solutions at a relatively constant pH. By releasing or absorbing H⁺, buffers minimize changes in pH. For example, human blood contains buffers that maintain a pH of 7.3-7.5 and slight changes in the pH of blood could result in complications or even death.

 Exercise 4.4a: Which is the Buffer?

Materials needed: sodium bicarbonate, sodium chloride, acetic acid, pH strips, two 50-mL beakers, 10-mL graduated cylinder, scissors, scale, weigh boat, gloves, safety goggles

1. Record your observations and results in the area below.
2. Cut pH paper into 2 cm strips while wearing gloves.
3. Weigh out 0.5 grams of sodium bicarbonate (NaHCO₃) and transfer to a beaker. Do the same with the sodium chloride (NaCl).
4. Measure 10 mL of water in the graduated cylinder, pour into the beaker containing the sodium bicarbonate, and swirl to mix. Repeat this process with the sodium chloride.
5. Test the pH of both solutions.
6. Measure 10 mL of acetic acid (CH₃COOH) in the graduated cylinder. Test the pH of acetic acid.
7. Pour 5 mL of acetic acid into the beaker containing the solution of NaHCO₃.
8. Pour the remaining 5 mL of acetic acid into the beaker containing the NaCl solution.
9. Test the pH of both solutions and record in the Observations section.
10. Wash all glassware and return items to your kit.

- Observations:

- Which solution acted as a buffer and why?

Checkpoint C

BIOL 1406 – Solutions Questions

Pre-Lab Questions

1. In a solution, the _____ is being dissolved.

2. You make a 40% salt solution – how much water did you add?
   a. 40%
   b. 60%
   c. 100%

3. _____ groups an organic molecule contains determine its characteristics?

4. A solution with a pH of 3 would be
   a. acidic.
   b. basic.
   c. neutral.

Post-Lab Questions

1. Why is it not possible to have a solution of acetic acid and sodium bicarbonate?

2. You stir a substance that contains carbonyl functional groups in water and it dissolves. What is occurring between the carbonyl groups and the water molecules to allow this?

3. What are the reactants and products in the dissociation of water?

4. If there are cations and anions in water, why does pure water have a pH of 7?

5. You are asked to determine if an unknown substance is an acid or base. How would you do this, based on what you did in this lab?

6. If you add a strong acid to blood, what would buffers do to maintain a pH of approximately 7.4?

EL CENTRO CAMPUS BIOL 1406 PBL
Biomolecules

Goals

1. Describe the structure of organic compounds.
2. Recognize different functional groups found in organic compounds.
3. Explain the general composition of biomolecules.
4. Contrast dehydration synthesis and hydrolysis.
5. Explain the importance of controls in biochemical tests.
6. Explain how to prevent contamination when performing chemical tests.
7. Describe the components of carbohydrates, lipids, proteins, and nucleic acids.
8. Perform tests to detect the presence of biomolecules.
9. Identify positive and negative results from the biomolecule tests.

Activity 5.1: Organic Compounds

In your last lab, you were introduced to compounds such as carbon dioxide (CO_2), water (H_2O), ionic salts, hydrogen (H_2), and oxygen (O_2). These are known as inorganic compounds and typically lack carbon-hydrogen bonds. On the other hand, **organic compounds** are usually formed by living organisms and contain carbon and hydrogen atoms. Methane (CH_4) is one of the simplest organic molecules, while the biological molecules you will be investigating in this lab are quite complex.

All life is said to be carbon-based due to carbon's four valence electrons, which can form covalent bonds with up to four other atoms (usually H, O, N, or another C). When carbon bonds with other carbon atoms, the **carbon skeletons** created serve as backbones to which other atoms or groups of atoms attach. Carbon skeletons can exist as a single carbon atom, a long chain, a branched structure, or a ring arrangement (Figure 5.1). Thus, the backbones of organic compounds range in complexity from simple methane to the benzene ring.

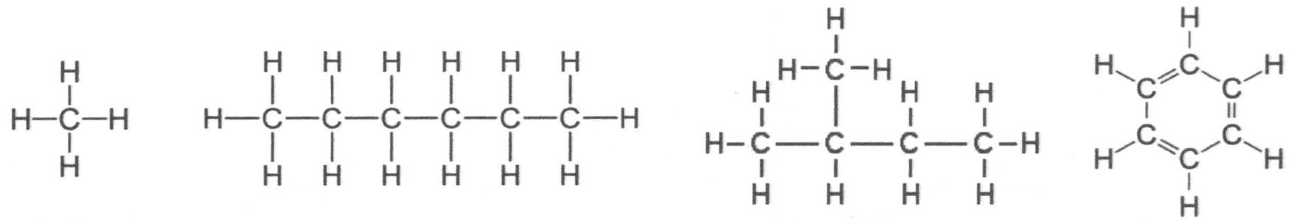

Methane	Hexane	Isopentane	Benzene
(CH_4)	(C_6H_{14})	(C_5H_{12})	(C_6H_6)

Figure 5.1. Types of Carbon Skeletons

Atoms other than hydrogen can bind to the carbon skeleton. These are typically groups of two or more atoms and are referred to as functional groups. **Functional groups** are usually chemically reactive and the types of functional groups an organic molecule contains determine its characteristics. Some of the most common functional groups are displayed in Table 5.1.

Table 5.1. Common Functional Groups

Group	Structure	Example	
Hydroxyl	–OH	Ethanol	
Carbonyl	–CO–	Acetone	
Carboxyl	–COOH	Acetic Acid	
Amino	–NH$_2$	Methylamine	
Phosphate	–H$_2$PO$_4$	Glycerate 3-phosphate	
Sulfhydryl	–SH	Butanethiol	
Methyl	–CH$_3$	Ethane	

✏ **Exercise 5.1: Analyzing Organic Compounds**   *Lecture*

• In addition to a phosphate, what other functional groups does glycerate 3-phosphate have?

Activity 5.2: Testing for Biologically Important Molecules

Complex organic compounds called **biomolecules** can be placed into one of four categories: carbohydrates, proteins, lipids, or nucleic acids. Biomolecules are often polymers, which are chains of simple molecules connected by covalent bonds. Each simple molecule, called a **monomer**, is linked to the next by **dehydration synthesis**, which is a type of condensation reaction. In dehydration synthesis a water molecule is removed to form a covalent bond. To break the bonds between monomers, a water molecule is added in the process of **hydrolysis**. Each of the four different biomolecules is composed of different types of monomers.

Scientists have developed many tests using **reagents** (substances used to detect another substance) to identify the different biomolecules. In order to perform these tests correctly, two different treatments must be completed to provide standards for comparison. The first treatment is called a **positive control** and contains the variable being tested for. For example, if you want to find out if a substance contains protein, you will first run the test on a known protein to make sure all the laboratory equipment is performing properly and to see what a positive reaction to the test will look like. The second treatment is the **negative control**, which does not contain the variable being tested for. For example, after you run the positive control test for a protein you will also run the test on water, which does not contain protein. A negative control is tested to ensure neither your reagent nor your test substance is contaminated and to see what a negative reaction to the test will look like.

Contamination is one of the main causes for the failure of experiments, so it is very important to prevent contamination in the lab. If you pour out too much of a chemical, do not pour it back into the original container without speaking with your instructor. Replacing the chemical might contaminate the entire container, resulting in not only the need to dispose of the entire container, but also increasing lab costs because more would need to be purchased. It is also very important to use one pipette for one chemical. Using one pipette to transfer two different types of chemicals will contaminate the original container and potentially introduce trace amounts of the wrong chemical into your experiment. Also, make sure all glassware is thoroughly cleaned between different experiments.

 Exercise 5.2: Chemical tests

- Why is distilled water used as a negative control for all tests?

- How can you avoid contaminating reagents or other substances during this lab?

Activity 5.3: Carbohydrates

Carbohydrates are molecules containing carbon, hydrogen, and oxygen. The monomers of carbohydrates are **monosaccharides**, the simplest form of a carbohydrate. When dehydration synthesis binds monosaccharides together, a specific type of covalent bond forms between the subunits: a **glycosidic bond**. If two or more monosaccharides are joined, they form a **polysaccharide**. A **disaccharide** is the simplest polysaccharide, as it has two monosaccharides.

 Exercise 5.3a: Draw Glucose   *Lecture*

Many different types of carbohydrates can be produced and utilized by living organisms. Of the monosaccharides, **glucose** is the main source of energy for cells, where it primarily exists as a ring structure (Figure 5.2). Many fruits contain high amounts of the sugar fructose, and our genetic material contains deoxyribose. Common disaccharides include **sucrose** (better known as table sugar, Figure 5.2) and lactose (the main sugar in milk). Plants store glucose as the coiled polysaccharide **starch** (Figure 5.2), but animals store their glucose as the polysaccharide **glycogen**.

The most common organic compound on Earth is **cellulose**, a structural polysaccharide found in the cell walls of plants. Humans cannot digest cellulose, but it serves as the "fiber" we require to help push food through our digestive systems.

Glucose - $C_6H_{12}O_6$

Sucrose (Glucose + Fructose) – $C_{12}H_{22}O_{11}$

Starch – Complex Carbohydrate

Figure 5.2. Common Carbohydrates

The polysaccharide starch can be identified with the **Iodine test**. In this test, iodine reacts with the coiled structure of the starch polymer producing a deep blue-black color.

 Exercise 5.3b: Iodine Test for Starch

Materials needed: 4 test tubes, iodine (Lugol's IKI), 4 substances in Table 5.2, gloves, goggles

1. Label four test tubes 1 through 4 with wax pencil.
2. Add 1 mL of **water** to test tube #1.
3. Add 1 mL of **starch** to test tube #2, **unknown A** to test tube #3, and **unknown B** to test tube #4.
4. Record the color of each substance in the "Color before iodine" column of Table 5.2.
5. Shake the iodine bottle gently.
6. Add 3 drops of iodine to each test tube and swirl to mix.
7. Record the color of each mixture in the "Color after iodine" column of Table 5.2.
➤ Cleanup:
   • Save test tubes #1 and #2 and keep them in your test tube rack for the remainder of the experiment. For the other tubes, empty contents of test tubes in the waste container provided, rinse, and reuse in the next experiment.

Table 5.2. Iodine Test Results

Tube	Substance	Color before iodine	Color after iodine
1	Water		
2	Starch		
3	Unknown A		
4	Unknown B		

- Which substance listed on Table 5.2 would be the **positive control**?

- Which substance listed on Table 5.2 would be the **negative control**?

- If you used this test on a monosaccharide, should you get a positive or negative result?

Checkpoint A

Activity 5.4: Proteins

Proteins are an important group of molecules composed of amino acids, performing a wide range of functions in living organisms. About 20 different types of **amino acids** exist, but all share the same general structure, as shown in Figure 5.3, with a central carbon atom attached to four different groups: a hydrogen atom (−H), an amino group (−NH$_2$), a carboxyl group (−COOH), and a variable side chain (−R) that defines the properties of the amino acid. Amino acids are linked together by **peptide bonds.** A peptide bond connects the amino acids glycine and alanine in Figure 5.3. A polypeptide chain forms as more amino acids are bound together. Interactions between side chains in the polypeptide result in the formation of the three-dimensional shape of the final protein.

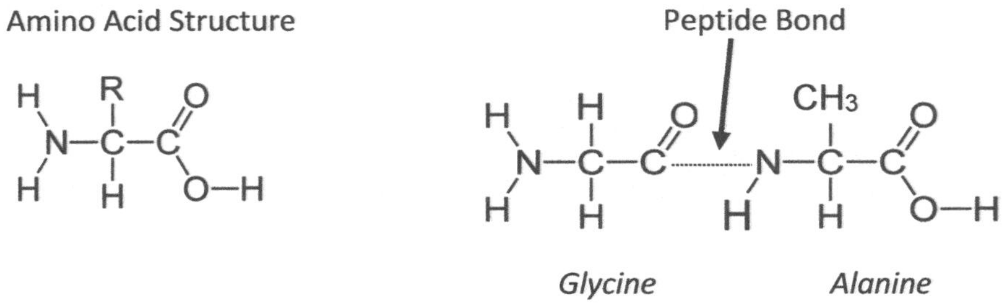

Amino Acid Structure

Peptide Bond

Glycine   Alanine

Figure 5.3. Amino acid structure (left) and peptide bond (right)

The **Biuret Test** identifies proteins, such as the albumin of egg whites, by reacting with the peptide bonds of a protein. The copper ions in the reagent form complexes with the nitrogen and carbon atoms of the peptide bonds. This reaction produces a color change to violet.

Biomolecules - 37

Exercise 5.4: Biuret Test for Protein

Materials needed: 4 test tubes, Biuret reagent, 4 substances in Table 5.3, gloves, goggles
Carefully read directions and note the difference between dropper and drops of chemicals.
1. Label 4 new test tubes #5 - 8
2. Add 1 mL of **water** to test tube #5
3. Add 1 mL of **albumin** to test tube #6, **unknown A** to test tube #7, and **unknown B** to test tube #8.
4. Add one DROPPER (20 drops) of Biuret reagent to first test tube and swirl.
5. Record the appearance of the mixture in test tube #1 in the "Initial color" column of Table 5.3.
6. Add one DROPPER (20 drops) of Biuret reagent to each of the remaining test tubes.
7. Record the appearance of the mixture in test tubes #6-8 in the "Initial color" column of Table 5.3.
8. After 5 minutes, record the appearance in the "Color after 5 min." column of Table 5.3.
➢ Cleanup:
   • Save test tubes #5 and #6 and keep them in your test tube rack for the remainder of the experiment. For the other tubes, empty contents of test tubes in the **waste container** provided.

Table 5.3: Biuret Test Results

Tube	Substance	Initial color	Color after 5 minutes
5	Water		
6	Albumin		
7	Unknown A		
8	Unknown B		

• Which substance listed on Table 5.3 would be the **positive control**?

• Which substance listed on Table 5.3 would be the **negative control**?

Checkpoint B

Activity 5.5: Lipids

Lipids are compounds that are insoluble in water but can be dissolved in nonpolar solvents such as acetone or ethanol. Lipids include fats and oils, phospholipids that form cell membranes, waxes, and steroids. Fats and oils are **triglycerides**, composed of three fatty acid chains attached to a glycerol molecule by **ester bonds** (Figure 5.4). Bonds between the carbons in the fatty acids determine if the triglyceride is a saturated or unsaturated fat. Double bonds in the fatty acids result in kinks in the chains (Figure 5.5). The fatty acids of **unsaturated fats**, such as oils, contain at least one double bond and the fatty acid chains cannot pack as closely together due to the kinks. The fatty acids of **saturated fats**, such as butter or lard, contain no double bonds. This results in straight fatty acid chains that can pack closely together.

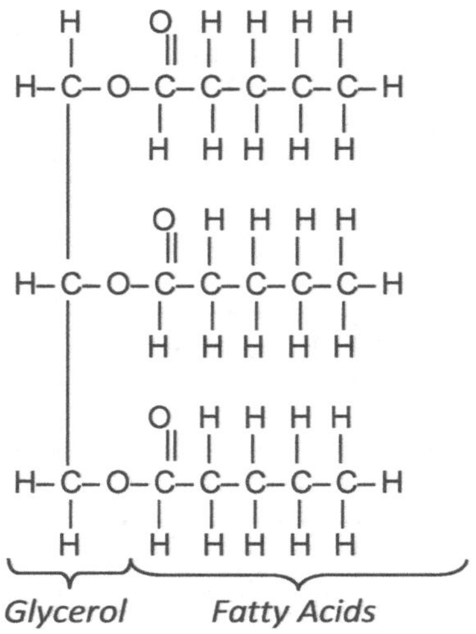

Figure 5.4. Triglyceride Molecule

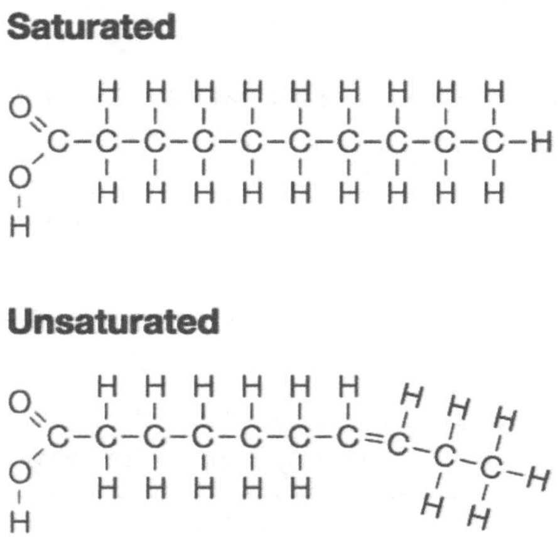

Figure 5.5. Saturated and Unsaturated Fatty Acids

The **Sudan Test** which utilizes Sudan III, a nonpolar reagent that is soluble in lipids. When Sudan III is added to a solution it will dissolve into and stain lipids a bright reddish-orange color.

 Exercise 5.5: Sudan Test for Lipids

Materials needed: 4 test tubes, Sudan III, distilled water, 4 substances in Table 5.4, gloves, goggles
SUDAN III IS HIGHLY FLAMMABLE, KEEP AWAY FROM HEAT

1. Label 4 new test tubes #9 -12
2. Add 2 mL of distilled water to test tube #9. Next add 10 drops of distilled water.
3. Add 2 mL of distilled water to test tube #10, then add 10 drops of corn oil.
4. Add 2 mL of distilled water, then 10 drops of **unknown A** to test tube #11. Add 2 mL of distilled water, then 10 drops of **unknown B** to test tube #12
5. Record the appearance of the test tubes in the "Initial appearance" column of Table 5.4.
6. Add 4 drops of Sudan III to each test tube and swirl.
7. Wait 5 minutes. Lipids are less dense than water, so look for a bright reddish-orange layer on top of the water. If there is no obvious orange layer, this is not a positive test.
8. Record the appearance in the "Appearance after 5 min." column of Table 5.4.
9. Cleanup:
    a. Save test tubes #9 and 10 and keep them in your test tube rack for the remainder of the experiment. Empty contents of all the other test tubes in the **organic waste container**. Do not rinse down the sink. Wipe off wax pencil markings.

Table 5.4. Sudan Test Results

Tube	Substance	Initial appearance	Appearance after 5 min.
9	Water		
10	Corn oil		
11	Unknown A		
12	Unknown B		

- Which substance listed on Table 5.4 would be the **positive control**?

- Which substance listed on Table 5.4 would be the **negative control**?

Checkpoint C

Activity 5.6: Summary of Biomolecule Tests

The test tubes you saved in your rack are the positive and negative controls. Examine each closely to make sure you understand what a positive result looks like for each test. In the table below, describe what the positive and negative results look like for each biomolecule test.

Table 5.5: Summary of positive and negative reactions

Biomolecule	Positive Result	Negative Result
Starch		
Proteins		
Lipids		

> Final cleanup: Pour the contents of the first two test tubes (from the iodine and Biuret test) in the waste container and the last test tube (from the Sudan test) in the **organic waste container**. Wipe off wax pencil markings. Place test tubes upside down in the racks by the sink.

In the table below, fill in the reagent that tested positive with each substance. Then, fill in which biomolecule that reagent detects. Hint: one substance is the negative control in all tests and should not have tested positive for any biomolecule.

Table 5.6: Overall Results for Biochemical Tests

Substance	What reagent yielded a positive result?	What biomolecule does the substance contain?
Water		
Starch		
Corn oil		
Albumin		
Unknown A		
Unknown B		

- Compare your results with another group. Do the results agree?

- Starch can be classified as one of the four main biomolecules, but it can also be placed in a more specific group based on its large number of monomers. Which group is this?

- What biomolecules did your unknowns contain?

- If you tested pepperoni pizza using the three different biomolecule tests, what do you think the results would be?

Checkpoint D

Activity 5.7: Nucleic Acids

Deoxyribonucleic acid (DNA) and ribonucleic acid (RNA) are two nucleic acids. DNA is the genetic material within all living organisms. **Nucleotides** are the monomers of nucleic acids and consist of a phosphate group, a pentose sugar, and a nitrogen-containing base. In Figure 5.6, **P** represents the phosphate group and **S** represents the sugar group. There are four different types of nitrogen-containing bases in DNA: adenine (**A**), cytosine (**C**), guanine (**G**), and thymine (**T**). In RNA, thymine is replaced by uracil (U).

A polynucleotide is formed when nucleotides bond. This bond between the phosphate of one nucleotide and the sugar of another nucleotide is called a **phosphodiester bond**. The phosphates and sugars make up the sugar-phosphate backbones of the polynucleotide strand. While RNA molecules consist of only one polynucleotide strand, DNA molecules typically possess two strands that run in different directions (Figure 5.6). In DNA, the nitrogen-containing bases on one strand form hydrogen bonds with nitrogen-containing bases on the other strand. The nitrogen-containing bases will only form bonds in certain pairs: adenine-thymine and cytosine-guanine.

There is no simple test for nucleic acids therefore you cannot test for nucleic acids in this lab.

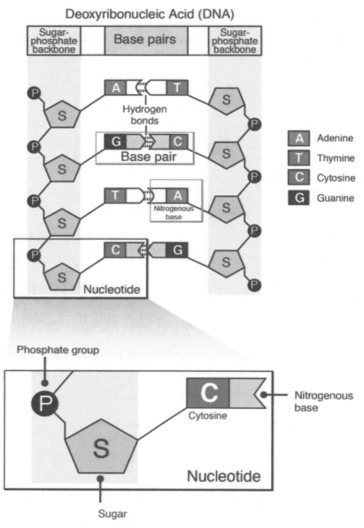

Figure 5.6. DNA structure

 Exercise 5.7: Nucleic Acids

- Should any of the substances you tested in the previous exercises contain DNA?

- If you conducted a test for the presence of DNA, what could you test to get a positive result?

BIOL 1406 - Biomolecule Questions

Pre-Lab Questions

1. Functional groups are attached to the carbon backbone of organic molecules and determine a molecule's properties.
    a. True
    b. False

2. Which molecule is not one of the four main biomolecules?
    a. Protein
    b. Carbohydrate
    c. Hydrochloric acid
    d. Lipid

3. A polymer is composed of what subunits?

    _____

4. What type of chemical reaction forms polymers?

    _____

5. Amino acids are the monomers of proteins.
    a. True
    b. False

Post-Lab Questions

1. Explain the difference between organic and inorganic molecules.

2. Starch and sucrose are both carbohydrates, but how do they differ?

3. Compare and contrast saturated and unsaturated fats.

4. Your classmate shows you the chemical structure for an organic molecule but cannot tell if it is a protein or a nucleic acid. What details would you point out to your classmate to help him out?

5. What types of bonds are found linking the monomers of the four different biomolecules? Name the general bond that is found in all biomolecules, then the specific bond used for each type.

6. On a molecular basis, how do the reagents used in the different tests react with their intended biomolecule? For example, how does iodine react with starch?

7. A friend shows you a picture of a biomolecule test result. How would you know what test was performed with this one picture?

Microscope

Goals
1. Demonstrate the correct way to carry a microscope.
2. Identify the parts of the compound microscope and describe their function.
3. Focus the microscope using different objective lenses.
4. Use the microscope to investigate magnification, orientation, and field of view.
5. Prepare a wet mount slide and observe living organisms in a drop of pond water.

Activity 6.1: Getting to Know Your Microscope

Microscopes are frequently used in the study of life because many biological organisms are too small to view with the unaided eye. The most commonly used microscope in an introductory biology lab is called a **compound light microscope**. The compound light microscope passes light through a specimen while multiple lenses magnify and focus the image of the specimen. Light microscopes can magnify images up to a thousand times their original size and allow us to see the most basic unit of biology: the cell.

A compound light microscope not only magnifies, but also improves resolution. **Magnification** refers to the ability of the lenses to increase the size of the specimen, while **resolution** is the ability to distinguish two points as separate objects. Magnification without improved resolution would result in a larger, yet blurred image of your specimen.

 Exercise 6.1a: Magnification and Resolution

Draw the below smiley face first with only magnification, then with both magnification and resolution. (Do this without using a microscope.)

<u>Magnified</u>   <u>Magnified & Resolved</u>

☺

 Exercise 6.1b: Microscope Transport
1. Locate a microscope in the cabinet. Your instructor may assign you a specific microscope to use throughout the semester.
2. To carry the microscope, grasp the arm with one hand and support the base with the other – microscopes are heavy and expensive!
3. Gently place your microscope near a power outlet on your table.
4. Plug the power cord of the microscope into the closest electrical outlet.

Exercise 6.1c: Anatomy of a Microscope

Identify the different components of your microscope and describe the function of each component per Figure 6.1 and Table 6.1.

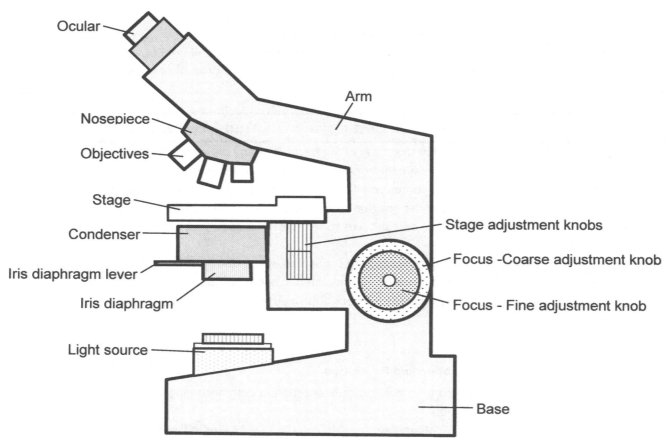

Figure 6.1. Compound Light Microscope

Table 6.1. Parts and Functions of a Compound Light Microscope

Part	Function
Arm	Supports lenses and stage
Base	Contains light source
Coarse adjustment knob	Use to focus with scanning (4X) objective
Condenser	Concentrates light on the specimen
Fine adjustment knob	Use to bring objects into sharp focus
Iris diaphragm	Regulates amount of light transmitted through specimen
Light source	Illuminates specimen
Nosepiece	Rotates to allow the use of different objective lenses
Objectives	Different lenses (4X, 10X, 40X 100X) mounted in nosepiece
Ocular	Houses ocular lenses (10X)
Stage	Platform with clip to hold microscope slide
Stage adjustment knobs	Moves slide left and right, forward and backward on stage

Exercise 6.1d: Focusing

1. Turn on the light source for the microscope and vary the intensity by turning the knob located on the arm of the microscope under the on/off switch. Notice that the light source brightens as you turn the knob clockwise. Put the light intensity all the way up for the following steps.
2. Look through the oculars and alter their spacing until you only see one image of a circle. This circle is called the **field of view**.
3. Adjust the light intensity, if necessary, by turning the knob.
4. Place a microscope slide of the **letter "e"** on the stage, securing it with the stage clip (see figure to the right).

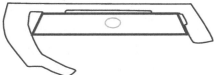

5. Move the slide using the stage adjustment knobs to make sure the letter "e" is centered over the condenser (hole in the stage allowing light to come through).

- Which stage adjustment knob (top or bottom) moves the slide right and left?

6. Now, swivel the 4X objective into place, then turn the coarse adjustment knob until the stage is in the lowest position.
7. While looking through the oculars, slowly turn the coarse adjustment knob counterclockwise until the letter "e" is in focus.
8. Use the fine adjustment knob to obtain the sharpest image.

- What is the orientation of the letter "e" when you look through the oculars compared to what you see with your unaided eyes?

- What direction does the <u>image</u> move when you use the stage adjustment knob to move the slide right?

Checkpoint A

 Exercise 6.1e: Magnification

The different lenses on the microscope have different degrees of magnification, per the table below. To determine the **TOTAL MAGNIFICATION** of an object, you multiply the magnification of the ocular lens by the magnification of the objective lens. For example, when using the oil immersion objective, the object is magnified 1000 times (10 x 100).

Lens	Magnification
Ocular	10X
Scanning	4X
Low Power	10X
High Power	40X
Oil Immersion	100X

1. Make sure the letter "e" is in the center of the field of view and that it is a clear image. (If it isn't, move the slide with the stage adjustment knobs and focus knobs until it is in focus.)
2. Once you've gotten a clear image of the letter "e" using the 4X objective, carefully swivel the 10X objective into place WITHOUT moving the focus knobs or stage. The objective will come close to the slide but will not touch a normal slide.

> **DO NOT USE THE COARSE OBJECTIVE KNOB TO FOCUS AFTER YOU HAVE SWITCHED FROM THE 4X OBJECTIVE!** ONLY USE THE FINE ADJUSTMENT KNOB WHEN USING THE 10X, 40X, AND 100X OBJECTIVES! Your microscope is **parfocal**, meaning it will retain the same focus when switching to different objectives.

3. Look through the oculars and use the fine adjustment knob to bring the letter "e" into sharp focus. Recenter the image if necessary.

- When you use your microscope to look at a specimen with the 4X objective, which lenses are utilized to magnify the image?

- Given the previous question, what is the TOTAL magnification of the letter "e"?

- How much larger should the image using the 10X objective be compared to the image using the 4X objective?

Exercise 6.1f: Contrast

Contrast increases our ability to recognize the details of a specimen by enhancing the difference between the light and dark parts of an image.

1. Move the iris diaphragm lever below the condenser all the way left.
2. While looking through the microscope, move the lever to the right gradually to find the best contrast of your image.
3. If the background seems grainy, use the black knob to the left of the condenser to adjust the position of the condenser. **NOT THE SMALL METAL KNOB.**
4. After you are finished viewing the slide, lower the stage as low as it will go with the coarse adjustment knob and carefully remove the slide.

- At what diaphragm lever position can you obtain the best view of the letter "e"?

Exercise 6.1h: Slide Box of Fun

Materials needed: slide box

The remaining slides in your slide box will be used to practice your microscope skills. Remember to always follow the steps below. In the spaces provided draw two of the specimens you view.

Always perform the following steps to view a slide:

1. Lower stage with coarse adjustment knob to the lowest position.
2. Swivel 4X objective into place.
3. Place slide on stage.
4. Secure slide with clip.
5. Position the object of interest on the slide over condenser.
6. Slowly focus using the coarse adjustment knob.
7. Change to 10X objective if necessary.
8. Recenter with stage adjustment knobs.
9. Focus with fine adjustment knob.
10. Repeat steps 8 & 9 with 40X objective if necessary.

<<<USE LENS PAPER TO CLEAN OCULARS AND OBJECTIVE LENSES IF NEEDED!>>>

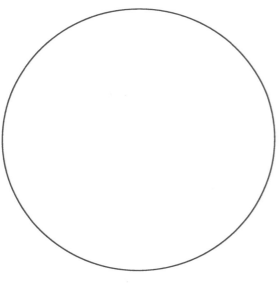   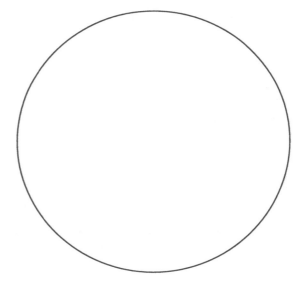

Specimen: _____   Specimen: _____

Objective used: _____   Objective used: _____

Total magnification of image: _____   Total magnification of image: _____

PUTTING AWAY A MICROSCOPE PROPERLY

1. Turn the light intensity to the lowest level and then turn off light source.
2. Make sure the stage is clean. Switch objective to 4X and lower the stage as low as it will go.
3. Wrap cord up.

Checkpoint B

BIOL 1406 - Microscope Questions

Pre-Lab Questions

1. A _____ light microscope uses two or more lenses and light magnify specimen.

2. What are the lenses in the eyepiece called?
   a. Ocular lenses
   b. Condensers
   c. Objective lenses

3. You can carry a microscope with one hand in the lab.
   a. True
   b. False

4. Microscopes are used to _____ a specimen to produce an enlarged image.
   a. Resolve
   b. Magnify
   c. Contrast

5. Which objective lens has a magnification of 10X?
   a. Scanning
   b. Low power
   c. High power

Post-Lab Questions

1. How are resolution and magnification different?

2. What is the total magnification for each of the objectives when used in combination with the 10X oculars?

3. Explain the difference between the condenser and the iris diaphragm.

4. Why should you use the coarse adjustment knob only with the scanning objective?

5. List the steps to view a microscope slide with the 40X (high power) objective and determine what the total magnification of specimen will be.

6. Which objective provides the largest field of view? In other words, if you were looking at a relatively large organism, with an area of about 2mm^2, which objective would you use to view the entire organism?

7. Before you put your microscope back into the cabinet you must turn off the light, change the objective to scanning, and wrap up the cord. Why?

Goals

1. Explain the principles of cell theory.
2. List the structural features shared by all cells.
3. Describe the differences between prokaryotic and eukaryotic cells.
4. Identify major cellular organelles and structures.
5. Explain the functions of the major organelles and structures.
6. Distinguish between plant and animal cells.

Activity 7.1: Units of Life

Life ranges from bacteria that can only be visualized with powerful microscopes to blue whales, the largest animals ever to have existed at 33 meters (108 feet) in length. Regardless of size, all life on Earth shares a fundamental similarity, which is expressed by the cell theory. **Cell theory** is a foundation of biological science and consists of two principles: (1) cells are the basic units of all living organisms and (2) cells arise from preexisting cells as hereditary information is transferred during cell division.

Although bacterial cells function independently while blue whales are made up of hundreds of trillions of cells working in concert, all cells include four components: a plasma membrane, DNA, cytosol, and ribosomes. The **plasma membrane** surrounds the cell, defining a boundary between the environment outside the cell and the cell contents. **DNA**, short for deoxyribonucleic acid, stores hereditary information in the structure of its molecules and is transferred from cell to cell during division. **Cytosol** is the intracellular fluid found within a cell while **ribosomes** are protein-synthesizing structures found suspended in the cytosol.

Based on structure, two major types of cells exist: prokaryotic and eukaryotic. **Prokaryotic** cells are usually less than 10μm (micrometers) in length and are believed to possess a structure similar to the first cells that existed 3.5 billion years ago. **Eukaryotic** cells typically range from 10 to 100μm and are more complex than prokaryotic cells. Membrane-bound **organelles** (intracellular components with specialized functions) are found in all eukaryotic cells.

 Exercise 7.1: Cell Similarities *Lecture*

- Despite their differences, both eukaryotic and prokaryotic cells must have which four basic components?

Activity 7.2: Prokaryotic Cells

Two of the three domains of life, Bacteria and Archaea, contain organisms composed of prokaryotic cells, also known as **prokaryotes**. Both can exist as single cells but are also capable of forming aggregate communities called biofilms, such as dental plaque. Bacteria can be found in every habitat on Earth and include species of many diverse groups: *Pseudomonas* and *Klebsiella* inhabit the intestines of humans and produce vitamin B12; the cyanobacterium *Oscillatoria* can readily be found in stagnant waters; *Lactobacillus* helps convert milk into yogurt; as well as many pathogens such as *Vibrio cholerae* (cholera) and *Mycobacterium tuberculosis* (tuberculosis). Archaea were first discovered in extreme environments, such as near-boiling hot springs. Genetically, these organisms are more closely related to eukaryotes, but perform the same biological functions as Bacteria due to their similar cellular structure.

Like all cells, prokaryotes must possess the four basic components mentioned in Activity 7.1. However, prokaryotes lack membrane-bound organelles, most notably a nucleus. Instead, most cellular processes occur in the cytosol along the interior of the cell membrane. A region called the **nucleoid** contains the majority of the cell's DNA. Surrounding the cell membrane is a rigid **cell wall** which contains the carbohydrate-amino acid polymer peptidoglycan. Bacteria may also produce a **capsule** external to the cell wall for further protection. Extensions of the cell membrane, or **pili**, used for attachment may extend through the cell wall and capsule. Many prokaryotes possess **flagella** for movement.

✎ **Exercise 7.2a: Identify Prokaryotic Cell Components**   *Lecture*

- Identify all structures in Figure 7.1.

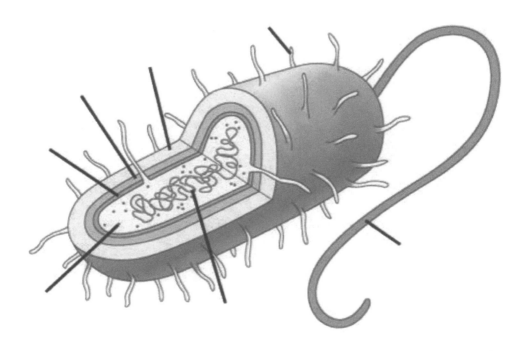

Figure 7.1. General Structure of a Prokaryotic Cell

Most bacteria and archaea must be magnified to a great extent to be properly examined. In combination with the oculars, the oil immersion objective on the compound microscope is capable of magnifying a specimen 1000 times its original size. Some bacteria live in colonies, such as *Oscillatoria*, a type of cyanobacteria that can undergo photosynthesis. Some cyanobacteria may be viewed using the high power objective on a compound microscope.

 Exercise 7.2b: Examining Prokaryotic Cells

Materials needed: compound microscope, lens paper, prepared slides of Oscillatoria.

1. Locate filaments of *Oscillatoria* using the scanning (4x) objective. The filaments may be dyed bright colors.
2. Switch to the low power (10x) objective to select one filament.
3. Switch to the high power (40x) objective to focus on the cells of the colony. With this objective and the oculars, the total magnification of the image is 400x. Notice the lines running across the filament. These lines are where the cell walls of two neighboring cells touch.

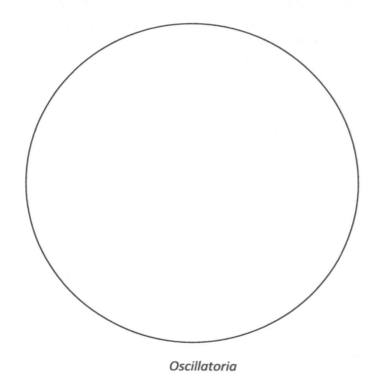

Oscillatoria

- Do the cells of Oscillatoria contain nuclei? Why or why not?

- What carbohydrate are the cells walls of *Oscillatoria* composed of?

Activity 7.3: Eukaryotic Cells

The third domain contains organisms composed of eukaryotic cells, also known as **eukaryotes**. Eukaryotes include unicellular and multicellular organisms that fall within one of four main groups of Eukaryota: animals, plants, fungi, and protists. Animals include multicellular heterotrophic organisms as simple as sponges or as complex as humans. Plants include not only large autotrophic green plants like the Giant Redwood, but also the nondescript moss. Fungi can be found as the mushrooms in an omelet, the mold on bread, or the yeast that produces the alcohol in beer and wine. Protists include a diverse array of organisms, from unicellular animal-like *Paramecium* and *Amoeba* to multicellular red seaweed.

Eukaryotic cells are generally larger and more complex than prokaryotic cells. The presence of a nucleus defines eukaryotes (from Greek – eu = true, karyon = nucleus), as does the rest of the membrane-bound organelles. The **nucleus** is surrounded by the double membrane of the **nuclear envelope**, separating the DNA from the rest of the cell. Within the nucleus lies a region called the **nucleolus** where ribosomes are assembled. Outside the nucleus, the organelles and cytosol comprise the **cytoplasm** that extends from the cell membrane to the nucleus. Eukaryotic cytosol is less viscous (more fluid) compared to that of prokaryotes and its constant movement, known as **cytoplasmic streaming**, allows organelles to interact with one another.

Extensions of the nuclear membrane form the **endoplasmic reticulum,** abbreviated as ER. The ER includes portions covered by ribosomes (rough ER) which synthesize proteins that then enter the interior space (lumen) where processing occurs. Other portions of the ER lack ribosomes and are referred to as the smooth ER. The functions of the smooth ER include lipid synthesis and drug detoxification. Many molecules produced by the ER are transported in spherical membrane-bound **vesicles** to the **Golgi apparatus**. Within the Golgi apparatus, the contents of the vesicles are released, further modified, and repackaged to be sent elsewhere in or out of the cell. The ER and Golgi apparatus produce **lysosomes**, large vesicles that contain digestive enzymes. The function of a lysosome is to break down complex molecules within the cell.

Mitochondria are the powerhouses of the cell, producing energy-storage molecules called ATP. ATP is needed by all cells to fuel the chemical reactions required for life. The **cytoskeleton** is a dynamic structure within the cytoplasm. The cytoskeletal elements are composed of protein fibers, which provide structural support and allow for movement. The three main elements - microfilaments, intermediate filaments, and microtubules - are identified by their protein composition. Many eukaryotes, notably unicellular organisms and the sperm of multicellular eukaryotes, possess cilia or flagella composed of microtubules for movement. **Cilia** are short cellular projections that produce a wave-like motion, whereas **flagella** are longer structures and typically propel cells using a whip-like motion.

All eukaryotic cells contain nuclei, cytoplasm, ER, Golgi apparatus, lysosomes, mitochondria, and a cytoskeleton in addition to the four basic structures found in all cells. However, different types of eukaryotic cells contain additional organelles for different purposes. You will examine two different types of cells – animal and plant cells – in the next two activities.

Exercise 7.3: Comparing Prokaryotes and Eukaryotes   *Lecture*

- What structures are found in eukaryotes, but not prokaryotes?

Activity 7.4: Animal Cells

Animal cells are eukaryotic but contain some structures not found in other cell types. For example, two centrioles are found exclusively in animal cells. **Centrioles** are short sections of microtubules that act as organizing centers for microtubules throughout the cell.

 Exercise 7.4a: Examining Animal Cell Components   *Lecture*

- Identify all structures in Figure 7.2.

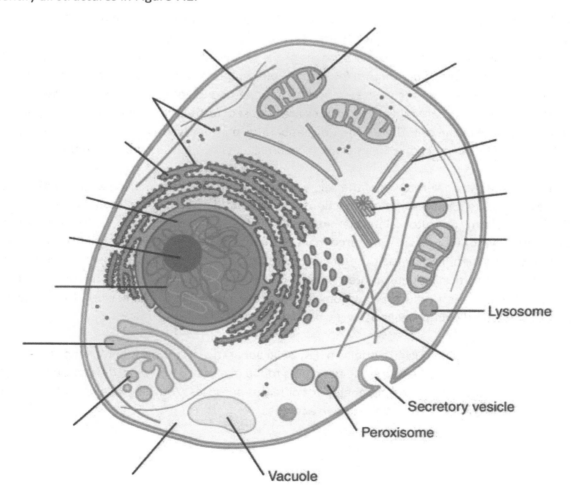

Figure 7.2. Model of "ideal" animal cell

Exercise 7.4b: Examining Animal Cell Components

Materials needed: compound microscope, prepared slides of bull sperm and epithelial cells

1. Examine slides of bull sperm and epithelial cells at a **total** magnification of 400x, using the correct series of focusing steps.
2. Draw a cell of each organism in the spaces below.
3. Label the organelles and cell structures you observe.

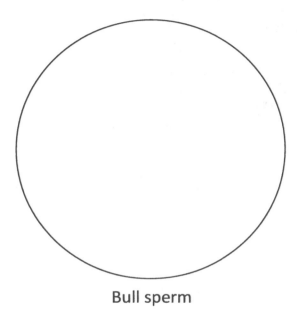

Bull sperm

Epithelial cells

Checkpoint A

Activity 7.5: Plant Cells

Plant cells do not have the centrioles found in animal cells but do possess many other distinctive structures. Surrounding the cell membrane of a plant is a **cell wall** composed of the carbohydrate cellulose. The cell wall supports and protects the plant cell. Occupying up to 80% of the interior of a plant cell is the **central vacuole**, surrounded by a membrane called the **tonoplast**. In addition to storing water, nutrients, pigments, and toxins, the central vacuole also acts like a lysosome to digest complex molecules. Also found only in plant cells are different types of plastids, which serve as sites of energy production or specialized storage structures. **Chloroplasts**, the most well-known plastid, contain the green pigment chlorophyll and are the sites of photosynthesis.

 Exercise 7.5a: Thinking about Plant Cell Components   *Lecture*

• If a plant cell has a cell wall, why does it also need a cell membrane?

Exercise 7.5b: Examining Plant Cell Components   *Lecture*

- Identify all structures in Figure 7.3.

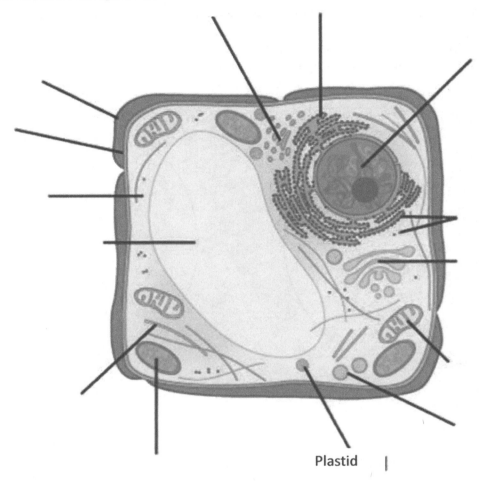

Plastid

Figure 7.3. Model of "ideal" plant cell

Exercise 7.5c: Examining Plant Cell Components

Materials needed: compound microscope, prepared slides of Syringa leaf, Elodea

1. Examine *Syringa* (lilac) leaf and *Elodea* (waterweed) slides at a **total** magnification of 400x, using the correct series of focusing steps.
2. Draw a cell for each organism and label the organelles and structures you observe.

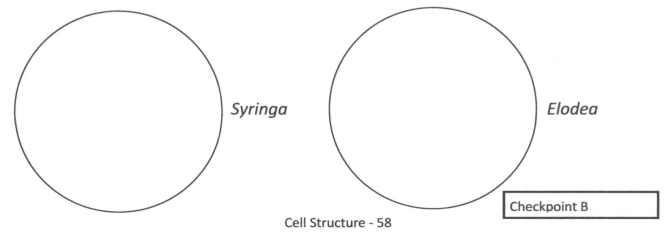

Syringa   *Elodea*

Checkpoint B

Activity 7.6: Mystery Cells

Models show us ideal cell types with clearly visible structures, but it is more difficult to distinguish cells types when examining real cells. While cells contain a wide variety of structures, it is difficult to resolve structures less than 500 nanometers in size using a light microscope.

 Exercise 7.6a: Form Hypotheses *Lecture*

Form two hypotheses regarding the characteristics you would use to identify plant and animal cells.

1.

2.

Exercise 7.6b: What Type of Cell am I?

Materials: box of mystery slides, compound microscope

1. Look at the mystery slides and categorize them as either plant or animal.

Slide #	Characteristics	Cell Type

- Were you able to visualize the characteristics you noted in your hypotheses? If not, why?

- Revise your hypotheses, if necessary.

Checkpoint C

BIOL 1406 – Cell Structure Questions

Pre-Lab Questions

1. What is the basic unit of life?

   _____

2. All cells contain a fluid called

   _____.

3. Bacteria are composed of what cell types?
   a. Prokaryotic
   b. Eukaryotic
   c. Animal

4. The most obvious structure eukaryotic cells possess that prokaryotic cells lack is/are
   a. ribosomes
   b. a cell membrane
   c. a nucleus

5. What structure do plant cells contain that allow for photosynthesis?

   _____

Post-Lab Questions

1. Explain the elements of the cell theory.

2. In your own words, write the basic definition for a <u>cell</u>.

3. Compare and contrast prokaryotic and eukaryotic cells.

4. What is the function of organelles?

5. Compare and contrast plant and animal cells.

6. A cell you are examining is surrounded by a cell wall and contains mitochondria as well as a nucleus. What type of cell is this and why?

Goals

1. Explain the difference between light and electron microscopes.
2. Describe how cells can be better visualized with the use of stains.
3. Perform techniques to observe the structure of live cells.
4. Identify major cellular components in live cells.
5. Compare the structure of animal, plant, and protist cells.

Activity 8.1: Cytology

Cytology is the study of cell structure and function. Cytologists, scientists who study cells, utilize a variety of instruments and techniques to visualize the microscopic world of the cell. At the smallest level of cell organization, the **ultrastructure** (detailed structure) of the cell can be examined with the use of an electron microscope. As you learned in the last lab, very few cellular structures can be observed with a light microscope. A light microscope can only magnify up to one thousand times, but an **electron microscope** uses a beam of electrons to magnify objects up to one million times their original size, which is necessary to observe the ultrastructure of cells.

It is possible to study large cellular structures and organelles with a light microscope (also called a compound microscope), especially if stains are used to increase contrast. **Contrast** is the degree to which details can be distinguished in comparison to their surroundings. By using different stains, one can color specific cell components, such as the nucleus or a cell wall, or the entire cell. Most stains must be used on non-living cells, but some can be used on living cells. In today's lab, you will look at the living cells of three different types of eukaryotes: plants, animals, and protists.

 Exercise 8.1: Ultrastructure   *Lecture*

If you wanted to observe ribosomes, what type of microscope would you use and why?

Activity 8.2: Examining Animal Cells

Epithelial tissue lines body cavities and surfaces of organs in the body. It is composed of thin layers of closely-packed cells and can be separated into two groups based upon the number of cell layers the tissue possesses. Simple epithelium is one cell thick, while stratified epithelium is several layers thick. The tissue that lines the inside of your mouth is composed of stratified epithelium, which can be easily sampled and examined.

Methylene blue is used to stain animal cells, such as the epithelial cells from the inside of your cheek, to increase the contrast of the nuclei and make them more visible. The molecules in the dye are attracted to nucleic acids and form complexes with the DNA molecule. For the next exercise, you will take a sample of your cheek cells, stain them with methylene blue, and observe them using a compound microscope.

 Exercise 8.2: Human Epithelial Cells

Materials needed: compound microscope, methylene blue, toothpicks, slide, coverslips, gloves, goggles, Kim wipes

1. Students must wear gloves and goggles during this activity.
2. Add one drop of methylene blue to the middle of a clean slide.
3. Use the flat side of a toothpick to gently scrape the inside of your cheek. You are taking a sample of <u>cells</u> and should not be able to easily see the tissue.
4. Gently touch the toothpick to the drop of dye on the slide and slowly stir for a few seconds.
5. Immediately dispose of the toothpick in a biohazard container.
6. Place a cover slip over the dye, per the instructions from the microscope lab. Make sure there are no air bubbles. If you have a lot of excess stain on the slide, absorb it with a Kim wipe.
7. Using the correct series of focusing steps, examine your epithelial cells using the high power (40x) objective.
8. Draw one or two of your epithelial cells and label as many cell components as you can visualize.
➢ DISPOSE OF THE SLIDE IN BIOHAZARD CONTAINER.

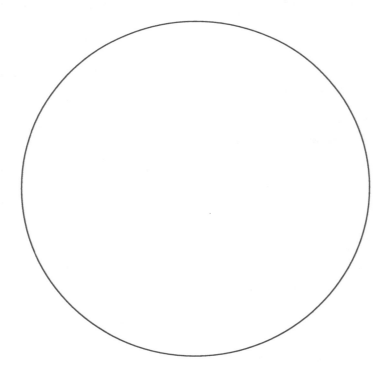

Human epithelial cell

Checkpoint A

Activity 8.3: Examining Plant Cells

Plant cells differ in many ways from animal cells, but the three most easily recognizable structures unique to plant cells are cell walls, central vacuoles, and plastids. Cell walls serve as a protective barrier, support the shape of the plant, prevent too much water from entering the cell, and help to retain water. Because the cell wall also inhibits the passage of substances into or out of the cell, the central vacuole functions as a storage organelle for water, nutrients, waste, and toxins. In addition, plant cells contain plastids for the storage and synthesis of additional materials. The plastid composition of a plant cell depends upon the function of the cell and may include chloroplasts, chromoplasts, and/or amyloplasts. **Chloroplasts** are the site of photosynthesis, the process in which the solar energy captured by the green pigment **chlorophyll** is used to convert carbon dioxide into simple sugars. Only plant cells normally exposed to light will contain chloroplasts. **Chromoplasts** synthesize and store pigments such as orange carotene, yellow xanthophylls, and red pigments. The cells of flowers and fruits tend to contain the highest amounts of chromoplasts. **Amyloplasts** synthesize and store the carbohydrate starch. When glucose is required for energy, amyloplasts will break the starch back into glucose molecules through hydrolysis. Large numbers of amyloplasts can be found in the fleshy parts of fruits and in the underground storage tissues of some plants.

To observe these and other plant structures, you will look at the cells from the leaf of *Elodea*, the epidermis of the fruit of a red bell pepper (*Capsicum annuum*), and a potato tuber (*Solanum tuberosum*). *Elodea* is an aquatic plant often used as aquarium vegetation with leaves only a few cell layers thick. The epidermis of the bell pepper fruit is only a few cells thick and will easily peel from the fruit after boiling. The tuber of a potato is a modified stem that is used for storage by the potato to survive from one season to the next.

Methylene blue and iodine will be used to better observe the structure of plant cells. As previously mentioned, methylene blue is used to visualize the nucleus. **Iodine** is a chemical indicator, turning from yellowish-brown to bluish-black in the presence of starch. This color change occurs when the molecules in iodine bind to the coiled structure of the starch molecule.

 Exercise 8.3a: Ideal Specimen

- Why would *Elodea* leaves and *Capsicum* epithelial tissue be ideal specimens to observe for the study of plant cells?

Exercise 8.3b: *Elodea*

Materials needed: compound microscope, Elodea, clean slide, coverslip, methylene blue

1. Add one drop of distilled water to the middle of a clean slide.
2. Place a single green leaf from *Elodea* on the slide and cover with a coverslip.
3. Using the correct series of focusing steps, examine the leaf with the 10x objective.
4. Switch to the 40x objective and find a single cell to observe.
5. Find the cell wall, central vacuole, and chloroplasts. The central vacuole is transparent but can be identified because it pushes organelles against the margins of the cell.
   6. As the cells warm up from the light source, take note of the **cytoplasmic streaming**. The movement of chloroplasts along the cell wall is obvious. Cytoplasmic streaming allows molecules to flow to all parts of the cell. Microfilaments may play a role in the movement.
7. Can you find any cells with a pink appearance? The central vacuoles of these cells contain a red pigment called anthocyanin.
8. Remove the coverslip and add a drop of methylene blue to better observe the nucleus.
9. Draw two *Elodea* cells and label as many cell components as you can visualize.
   - After you are finished with the slide, dispose of it in the **glass disposal container**.

Elodea cells

- During cytoplasmic streaming, are all the organelles flowing at the same rate and in the same direction?

Checkpoint B

Exercise 8.3c: *Capsicum*

Materials needed: Capsicum (pepper) epidermis, slide, coverslip, forceps

1. Add one drop of distilled water to the middle of a clean slide.
2. With forceps or fingernail, peel the epidermis layer from a small section of a red bell pepper.
3. Place epidermis on the slide and cover with coverslip.
4. Using the correct series of focusing steps, examine the epidermis with the 10x objective.
5. Switch to the 40x objective and find a single cell to observe.
6. Find the cell wall and chromoplasts. Draw and label several cells below.
7. After you are finished with the slide, dispose of it in the **glass disposal container**.

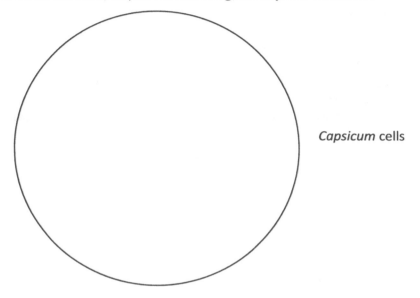

Capsicum cells

 Exercise 8.3d: Potato

Materials needed: demonstration slide of potato tuber stained with iodine

1. A thin slice of potato has been stained with iodine to better view the amyloplasts.
2. Draw a few cells below, labeling the amyloplasts.

Potato cells

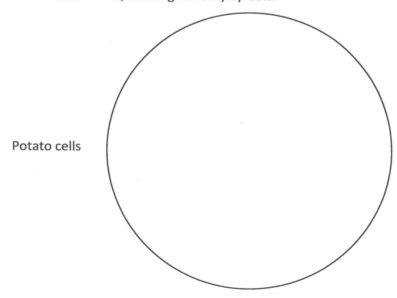

Checkpoint C

Activity 8.4: Examining Protist Cells

Protists are a highly diverse group of organisms. Like animals and plants, protists are eukaryotes with cells containing a nucleus and organelles. Some protists, like algae, are photosynthetic, while others are active consumers, like *Paramecium*. Other protists might remind you of a fungus. While many are unicellular they can also be amazingly complex. Explore the complexity of protists by examining *Paramecium*, a well-known unicellular protist. *Paramecium* move and eat with the use of the cilia covering the outside of their cell membrane. Other protists may also be available for examination.

 Exercise 8.4: Protists

Materials needed: compound microscope, cultures of Paramecium, microscope slides, coverslips.
1. Use a dropper to obtain *Paramecium* and place on a slide. Add a coverslip.
2. Locate a *Paramecium* using the scanning objective.
3. Examine the *Paramecium* with the 10x objective.
4. Draw the *Paramecium* cell and label as many cell components as you can visualize.
5. Follow the same procedure to examine other protists in the mixed protist culture.
6. Dispose of slides in the **glass disposal container**.

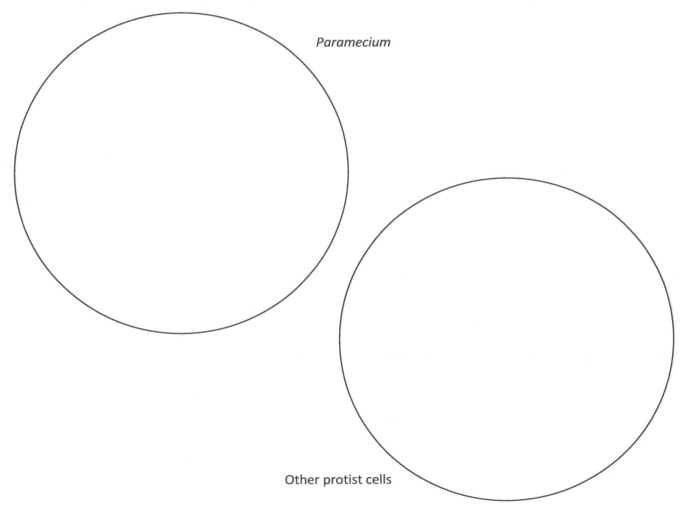

Paramecium

Other protist cells

BIOL 1406 – Techniques in Cytology Questions

Pre-Lab Questions

1. The degree to which details can be distinguished in comparison to their surroundings is called

   _____

2. Which dye is used to stain the nuclei of animal cells?
   a. Methylene blue
   b. Iodine
   c. Chlorophyll

3. Humans are composed of animal cells.
   a. True
   b. False

4. *Elodea* and most plants are green because their cells contain what organelle?

   _____

Post-Lab Questions

1. How did the use of stains improve the contrast of the different cell structures and organelles?

2. Which cell components could you easily observe in all the cells you examined in today's lab?

3. Compare and contrast the results of the methylene blue and the iodine staining techniques.

4. Compare and contrast the cell components of *Elodea*, *Capsicum*, and potato.

5. How did the movements of the various protists differ?

6. For each of the specimens observed today, name one important cell component you could have observed with an electron microscope.

EL CENTRO CAMPUS BIOL 1406 PBL
Membranes

Goals
1. Define and identify solvents, solutes, and solutions.
2. Describe the structure of cell membranes.
3. Determine the effects of temperature and concentration on diffusion.
4. Compare and contrast diffusion and osmosis.
5. Describe the different states of tonicity.
6. Explain the response of animal cells under different tonicities.
7. Compare and contrast this with the response of plant cells under different tonicities.

Activity 9.1: Diffusion

The majority of a cell consists of water, which is referred to as the solvent of life. A **solvent** is the liquid medium in which a substance, the **solute**, is dissolved. As a result, a **solution** is produced, which is a combination of solvent and dissolved solutes. The cytosol in a cell is a **solution**; water is the solvent while ions, molecules, and other complex compounds are the solutes. Solute particles are in constant motion due to the kinetic energy present in all atoms and molecules. This motion, referred to as **Brownian motion**, is the driving force behind diffusion. **Diffusion** is the movement of substances from higher concentrations to lower concentrations. For example, if a sugar cube is placed in a glass of water the individual sugar molecules will move down a **concentration gradient** as they dissolve, resulting in a solution that is relatively uniform in its sugar concentration. Factors such as temperature, solute concentration, and molecular weight of the solute affect the rate of diffusion.

 Exercise 9.1a: Solutions   *Lecture*

- Describe what is happening on a molecular level as sugar dissolves in water, resulting in a solution of sugar water. Be sure to include the terms: solution, solute, solvent, Brownian motion, diffusion, and concentration gradient.

Exercise 9.1b: Miranda's Iced Tea Problem Revisited   *Lecture*

Do you remember Miranda? If you recall, Miranda had a problem when we examined the scientific method during the first lab unit. While making iced tea, Miranda noticed that when she added sugar and stirred, most of the sugar did not dissolve. Instead, the sugar settled to the bottom of the pitcher. So she developed a hypothesis that using hot tea would cause the sugar to dissolve more readily. Miranda then set up an experiment by making three cups of tea in clear cups. Shen added two tablespoons of sugar when the cups were at different temperatures. For the first cup, she added the sugar while the tea was still very hot. The second cup she allowed to cool to room temperature before adding the sugar. The third cup she put in the refrigerator for 5 minutes before adding the sugar. The results of her experiment were interesting. No undissolved sugar was seen at the bottom of the first cup. A small amount of sugar was seen at the bottom of the second cup. A larger amount of sugar was seen at the bottom of the third cup.

Let's now examine her results at a molecular level!

- Identify the solvent(s) and solute(s) in iced tea.

- What was happening on a molecular level to allow the sugar to dissolve in the tea (which is mostly composed of water)?

- Why does the sugar dissolve at different rates in the three different temperatures?

Table sugar is sucrose, with a chemical formula of $C_{12}H_{22}O_{11}$ and a molecular weight of 342.3 g/mol. Sucralose is an artificial sweetener with a chemical formula of $C_{12}H_{19}Cl_3O_8$ and a molecular weight of 397.6 g/mol.

- If Miranda placed the same amount of both sucrose and sucralose in the hot tea, which should diffuse faster? Why?

✏️ **Exercise 9.1c: Diffusion and Size**   *Lecture*

Lugol's iodine solution (often used as an antiseptic) is a solution of elemental iodine and potassium iodide in water. Elemental iodine (I_2) has a molecular weight of 254 g/mol, while potassium iodide (KI) has a weight of 266 g/mol. Starch is a polysaccharide produced by plants and consists of numerous glucose molecules bound together by glycosidic bonds. Different forms of starch have differing numbers of glucose units, ranging from a few hundred to many thousands of units (Figure 9.1: The *n* for the middle glucose unit in amylopectin and amylose implies there are a varying amount of those units). Each glucose unit has an approximate molecular weight of 164 g/mol. A single glucose molecule is 180 g/mol, but this is before dehydration synthesis (i.e. a free, unbound glucose molecule).

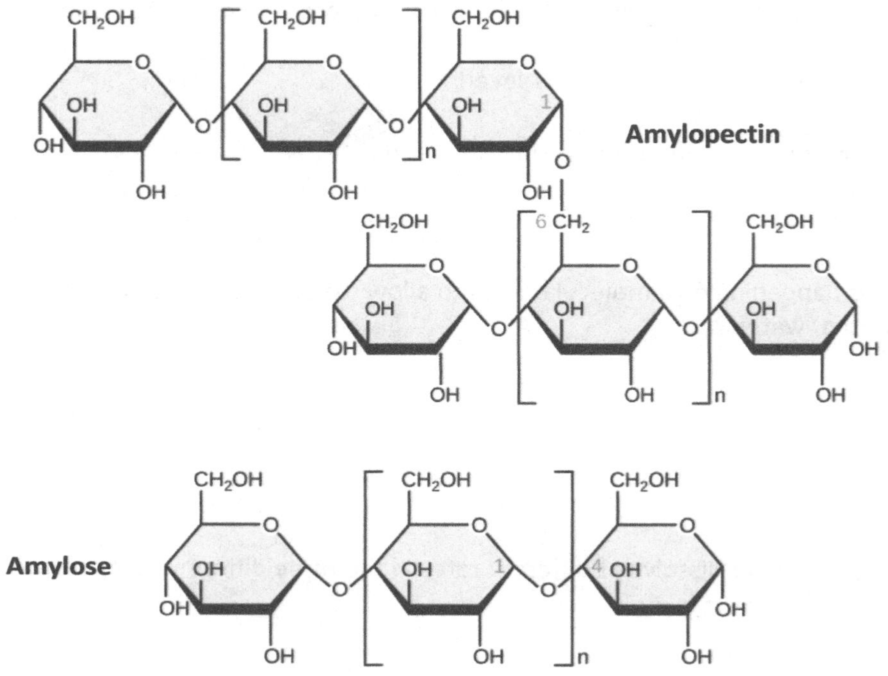

Figure 9.1. Two different forms of starch: Amylopectin and amylose

- Which would diffuse faster: the iodine-containing molecules found in the Lugol's iodine solution or a molecule of starch? Why?

Activity 9.2: Selectivity

To enter or exit the cell, solutes must pass across the cell membrane, which is composed of a **phospholipid bilayer**. The hydrophilic heads of the phospholipids face towards the inside and outside of the cell, while the hydrophobic tails cluster between the heads to avoid the aqueous environment. This arrangement allows the cell membrane to be **selectively permeable**, with the ability to regulate the passage of substances into and out of the cell. Only small nonpolar molecules, such as oxygen, carbon dioxide, and some steroids, can diffuse easily through the phospholipid molecules of the cell membrane. Other molecules utilize transport proteins to enter or exit the cell. Some proteins allow **passive transport** by providing a location through which molecules can move down their concentration gradients (diffusion). Substances that must move against their concentration gradients require **active transport**, in which energy is used.

 Exercise 9.2a: What's in a Cell Membrane?   *Lecture*

Draw a phospholipid bilayer then insert some proteins and other components found in a typical cell membrane. Label important structures and regions.

We can demonstrate the selectivity of cell membranes with the use of dialysis tubing. Dialysis is the removal of certain solutes from a solution by use of a membrane, and the tubing used has pores that will only allow the passage of small molecules. The dialysis membrane is similar to a cell membrane, but keep in mind that a living membrane (which is much more complex) also restricts most polar molecules and contains transport proteins.

 Exercise 9.2b: You Shall Not Pass… Across the Membrane   *Lecture*

In the next experiment, you will be examining how size is one factor that determines whether or not a molecule will pass through the phospholipid bilayer of a cell membrane. Below, you will formulate a hypothesis regarding which substances should be able to cross a dialysis membrane: starch and/or iodine. Then you will make a prediction, explaining what results you should observe if your hypothesis is correct. (Hint: recall what reaction you should see when iodine comes into contact with starch.)

Hypothesis:

Prediction:

Exercise 9.2c: Membrane Selectivity Experiment

Materials needed: 1 piece of dialysis tubing, 2 pieces of string approximately 15 cm long, starch solution, iodine, 1 400-mL beaker, pipette

READ CAREFULLY: NOTE THE DIFFERENCE BETWEEN DROPPERS AND DROPS!!

1. Obtain string and soaked dialysis tubing.
2. Roll the tubing between thumb and finger to open. Wet with water if too dry.
3. Seal one end of the tubing by folding and tying with string (See Figure 9.2).
4. Using a pipette, add 2 mL of starch solution into the tubing.
5. Seal the other end of the tubing to create a bag by folding the end and tying with string.
6. Rinse bag with tap water. This bag is your *simulated cell*.
7. Place bag in beaker and add 100 mL of tap water and 2 DROPPERS of iodine.
8. Leave bag in beaker for 15 minutes.
9. Draw arrows on Figure 9.2 to indicate what substance diffused through the membrane and the direction of diffusion observed in the beaker.
10. Dispose of dialysis bag in the trash when the experiment is completed.

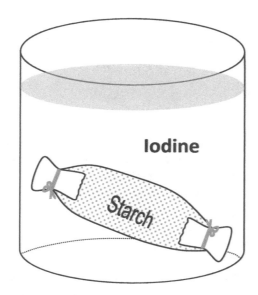

Figure 9.2. Membrane Selectivity Setup

-   Consider what substances you investigated. Does this experiment examine osmosis? Explain why or why not.

-   Did the experimental results cause you to reject or accept your hypothesis? Explain why.

Checkpoint A

Activity 9.3: Osmosis in Animal Cells

Cells require water in great quantities, yet water is a polar substance and cannot easily cross the cell membrane. This problem is solved by transport proteins called **aquaporins**, which regulate the flow of water. When water diffuses across a selectively permeable membrane, **osmosis** is occurring. As with any substance, water must move down its concentration gradient – from a region of high water concentration to a region of low water concentration. Water passes easily through a cell membrane because of the vast number of aquaporins present.

The surrounding environment can have an effect upon the movement of water into or out of a cell. **Tonicity** describes the ability of a solution to cause a cell to gain or lose water and is determined by rthevelative solute concentrations between the cell and its environment. Solutes that can diffuse across the membrane do not affect tonicity because they will diffuse, resulting in equal concentrations on both sides of the membrane. Only those solutes that cannot diffuse across the membrane influence tonicity. The three classifications of tonicity are hypertonic, hypotonic, and isotonic. A **hypertonic** solution contains a higher concentration of solutes compared to another solution, while a **hypotonic** solution contains a lower concentration of solutes. **Isotonic** solutions have equal concentrations of solutes.

For example, if an animal cell containing a concentration of 0.9% salt is placed in a 5% salt solution, the surrounding environment is hypertonic to the cell. The salt cannot move across the membrane and as a result the water in a cell moves to the area of lower water concentration – out of the cell – until the two solutions are of equal concentration. This loss of water causes the cell to shrivel or **crenate**.

 Exercise 9.3a: What's the Tonicity?   *Lecture*

Sucrose cannot diffuse across a cell membrane. With this knowledge, answer the following questions using the tonicities in Beaker A.

- What is the *tonicity* of the solution surrounding the animal cell?

- What is the *tonicity* of the solution within the cell?

- What is the water *concentration* surrounding the cell?

- What is the water *concentration* in the cell?

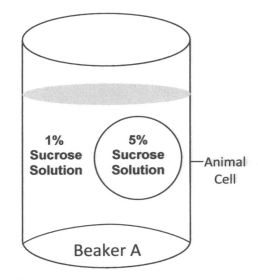

- In which direction will the water flow and as a result, what will happen to the cell?

In the next exercise you will demonstrate osmosis by placing three simulated animal cells into three different solutions. The three simulated animal cells will contain the same concentration of solutes while the surrounding solutions (extracellular fluid) will differ. For this experiment, sucrose will be the solute used to create the various solutions. Figure 9.3 shows the experimental design that you will duplicate with your simulated cells.

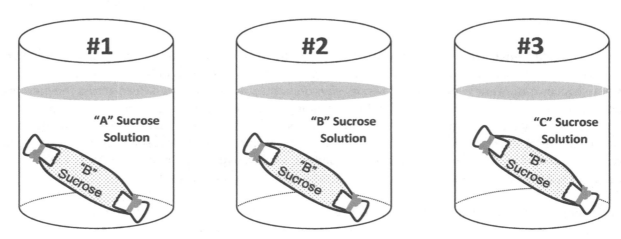

Figure 9.3. Osmosis Demonstration Experimental Setup

Solution A contains 1% sucrose. Solution B contains 25% sucrose. Solution C contains 50% sucrose. Draw arrows in Figure 3 to represent the predicted direction of water movement. Using this information, fill in Table 1 below to reflect the experimental design and your predictions.

Table 9.1. Osmosis Experimental Setup and Predictions (**to be done in Lecture**)

Cell #	Tonicity of *Cell*	Tonicity of *Extracellular Fluid*	Predicted Direction of Water Movement	Predicted Change in Mass of Cell: Gain/Loss/No Change
1				
2				
3				

- Compare your answers with those of your classmates. Do you agree?

- Concept check: what type of passive transport is being examined in this experiment?

Exercise 9.3b: Osmosis in Simulated Animal Cells

Materials needed: 3 pieces of dialysis tubing, 6 pieces of string or clips, 1%, 25%, & 50% sucrose solutions, 3 beakers (400-mL), electronic scale, pipette, china marker

1. Obtain string and soaked dialysis tubing.
2. Roll the tubing between thumb and finger to open. Wet with water if too dry.
3. Seal one end of the tubing by folding and tying with string.
4. Using pipette, fill with 5 mL of the 25% sucrose solution.
5. Seal the other end of the tubing by folding the end and tying with string. Try to remove air bubbles before tying the string because air bubbles will cause the bag to float.
6. Rinse bag with tap water, pat dry and <u>weigh</u> – record mass in Table 9.2.
7. Place bag in beaker labeled **#1** and add 100 mL of the 1% sucrose solution.
8. Repeat process to create two more bags, each with 2 mL of the 25% sucrose solution.
9. <u>Weigh</u> and place second bag in beaker labeled #2 and add 100 mL of the 25% sucrose solution.
10. <u>Weigh</u> and place third bag in beaker labeled C and add 100 mL of the 50% sucrose solution.
11. After 15 minutes, remove bags, rinse, dry, and <u>weigh</u> – record mass in Table 9.2.
12. Draw arrows on Figure 4 to indicate the direction of osmosis as shown by the results.
13. Dispose of dialysis bags in trash and clean workstation thoroughly.

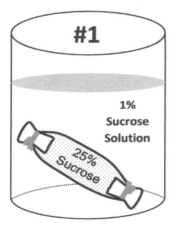 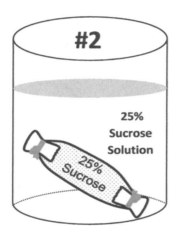 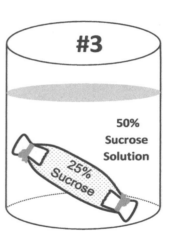

Figure 9.4. Osmosis Demonstration Setup

Table 9.2. Osmosis Results

Cell #	Initial mass (g)	Final mass (g)	Change in mass (g)	Water Loss or Gain?	Do Results Agree with Predictions?
1					
2					
3					

<u>**Note**</u>: Make sure to thoroughly clean your workstation after completing Exercise 9.3b; the sucrose solutions are extremely sticky.

Checkpoint B

Activity 9.4: Osmosis in Plant Cells

Plant and animal cells differ in regards to their responses to osmosis. The cell wall prevents plant cells from swelling and shrinking the way animal cells do. When a plant cell gains water, the cell (plasma) membrane will exert **turgor pressure** upon the cell wall. When the pressure reaches a certain level, water can no longer flow into the cell, even if the solutions inside and outside the cell are not isotonic. At this point, the cell has become **turgid**; this is the preferred condition of plant cells. When a plant cell loses water, the flexible cell membrane pulls away from the rigid cell wall, a condition is known as **plasmolysis**.

 Exercise 9.4: Observing Osmosis in Plant Cells (Optional)

Materials needed: compound microscope, Elodea, *clean slide, cover slip, 40% sodium chloride (NaCl) solution, distilled water.*

1. Obtain a leaf from Elodea, prepare a wet mount slide, and top with coverslip.
2. Following standard microscopy procedures, focus on one cell using the high-power (40x) objective. Draw a "normal" cell below.
3. Lower stage, remove coverslip, and add 1 drop of 40% NaCl solution.
4. Replace coverslip and bring cells back into focus using the high-power (40x) objective. Draw a "plasmolyzed" cell.
5. Lower stage, remove coverslip, dry off the leaf, add distilled water and replace coverslip.
6. Focus on cells again using the high-power (40x) objective and watch as cells go back to a "normal" state. This occurs at a slower rate than plasmolysis.

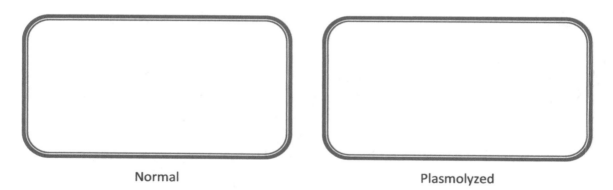

| Normal | Plasmolyzed |

- Describe how the cells appear under "normal" and "plasmolyzed" conditions.

- Compared to the cell, what type of solution is the 40% NaCl (isotonic, hypertonic, hypotonic)?

Checkpoint C

BIOL 1406 - Membranes Questions

Pre-Lab Questions

1. When a substance moves from an area of greater concentration to an area of lesser concentration, this is called

   _____

2. Higher temperatures should increase the rate of diffusion.
   a. True
   b. False

3. Osmosis is the diffusion of _____ across a membrane.

4. Which lipid molecules are cell membranes primarily composed of?
   a. Cholesterol
   b. Saturated fats
   c. Phospholipids

5. Hypertonic, isotonic and hypotonic describe the _____ of solutions.

Post-Lab Questions

1. Suppose you placed a water-soluble red dye and a water-soluble blue dye in water at the same time and the blue dye diffused throughout the water quicker. What can you conclude about these two molecules? (hint: this is not about tonicity)

2. Compare and contrast the membranes of dialysis tubing and a living cell.

3. Could iodine or starch diffuse across the dialysis membrane? How did the experiment demonstrate this?

4. How does membrane selectivity (also known as selective permeability) and osmosis differ? Which experiment investigated membrane selectivity? What about osmosis?

5. Explain why the dialysis bags lost or gained weight in the osmosis experiment.

6. When placed in hypertonic solutions, how do the responses of plant and animal cells differ?

Goals
1. Define plagiarism.
2. Recognize proper paraphrasing.
3. Describe how to find a valid reference.

Activity 10.1: What is Plagiarism?

When you present another person's work as your own you have committed **plagiarism**. Even if you did not do it deliberately, you still have plagiarized because whoever is reading the words you copied assumes you wrote those words. In a course, your instructor is the one assuming you wrote those words and must use them to evaluate your understanding of the class material. By submitting plagiarized work, you are misrepresenting your knowledge of the concepts you need to know. For your instructor to assess your true understanding, you must present work that is in your own words. However, that does not mean you cannot use other materials such as your textbook or a handout as a reference. Valid references, supplied or approved by your instructor, are necessary to help you learn the material required for a course.

When presenting facts in a paper, you may either paraphrase your reference or quote directly from it. In both cases, however, the source of the fact must be cited to avoid plagiarism. Some information is deemed common knowledge and does not require citation.

Paraphrasing

To **paraphrase** is to restate something you have read or heard in your own words. When you write a paper for a class, paraphrasing is important because it demonstrates that you understand a particular concept. This is often not an easy task. Sometimes the reference will explain the concept in such a simple and concise manner, it seems impossible to state it any other way. In this case, go over the source material until you fully understand the concept, then spend some time deciding the best way to explain the concept to a friend. Write down your explanation and compare it the source. Your version may be longer and less elegant, but accuracy is much more important. In other instances, the reference may be overly complicated or use unfamiliar terminology. This makes it difficult to truly understand the concept, let alone restate it. Instead of beating your head against a wall, find another credible source. If you still have difficulties, make sure you understand the definitions of all the terms. In your paper, clarify the concept by using simple language and defining terms that were confusing to you. Since you obtained information from a reference and restated it, citing the source is still necessary.

Quotations

In English or history classes, students write papers that often include quotations. Quotations present important elements of an artist's work or can be used to support an argument. In the technical writing that is used in biology, quotations are seldom used because it is extremely important for the author to show that they understand the material they are writing about. Unfortunately, quotations can be easily misused if the author only presents a quotation to explain a concept. Therefore, most instructors in introductory classes either do not allow quotations or require a restatement of the quotation in the author's own words.

Common knowledge

If most people are aware of a certain fact or if a phenomenon is easily observable, the information would be considered common knowledge. Say you stated that the sky was blue in your paper for a class. You would not need to cite any sources because consulting a reference to learn the information is not required. You would easily look outside and see that the sky is blue.

 Exercise 10.1a: Paraphrasing

Original

The atom is the basic unit of matter and consists of three different stable subatomic particles: protons, neutrons, and electrons. Negatively charged electrons orbit the nucleus, which contains positively charged protons and neutral neutrons. Electrons occupy certain shells around the nucleus based on their energy levels.

Three different superheroes try their hand at paraphrasing the paragraph above. Use your knowledge of paraphrasing to pick the valid restatement.

Thor

Atoms are elementary components of matter and consist of three dissimilar stable subatomic elements: protons, neutrons, and electrons. Negatively charged electrons circle the nucleus, which holds positively charged protons and neutral neutrons. Electrons inhabit particular shells around the nucleus based on their energy stages.

Black Widow

An atom has three different subatomic particles, which are electrons, protons, and neutrons. The nucleus has neutral neutrons and positively charged protons. Negatively charged electrons orbit the nucleus and occupy shells around the nucleus based on energy levels. Atoms are the basic unit of matter.

The Hulk

Matter is made up of atoms. The nucleus of an atom has protons with a positive charge and neutrons with a neutral charge. Electrons have a negative charge and are not in the nucleus. Electrons circle the nucleus in shells and because they have different levels of energy, the electrons are in different shells.

- Which restatement attempt is a good example of paraphrasing and why?

- For the other two attempts, list the problems.

Exercise 10.1b: Plagiarism Video

Your instructor will show you a video on plagiarism and may have you fill out a worksheet.

Activity 10.2: Detecting Plagiarism

For some written assignments your instructor will require that you upload a file of your work so that a program can check for plagiarism. The program conducts a search of the internet, previously uploaded work from past semesters, and any uploaded files for the current semester. A report is generated and if any sections of the work matches another entity, the source file is identified as well as the percentage of matching material. Your instructor will go through the report and determine if there is valid evidence of plagiarism. There are often matches for references, which is no cause for concern. If plagiarism is found in the content of the paper, however, a meeting will be arranged to discuss the misconduct. Penalties may include a deduction from the total number of points, a grade of zero for the entire assignment, or a meeting with the dean if the situation warrants.

 Exercise 10.2: We have a match!

Your instructor will show you the plagiarism report for two papers. Explain why one shows clear evidence for plagiarism regarding content, while the other does not.

Activity 10.3: Citing your Source

Citing references is not difficult, but you must know the rules you need to follow. A certain format or style is used when writing a paper. MLA format is used in the majority of non-science fields, while APA format (or some variation) is favored in most science fields. Your instructor will assign a certain format, as well as detailed instructions for any additional rules that need to be followed.

In-text citation, also referred to as parenthetical citation, lets the reader know where you obtained specific information. It is important to understand that citing your sources does not give you the right to copy that source. You are still required to paraphrase (or use quotes per the format, if allowed) in order to avoid plagiarism. Since you will most likely not be quoting from your source, you will be referencing general information from a textbook, handout, journal article, etc. For this type of citation, you will use the last name of the author and the year published in parentheses. If there are more than two authors, the follow format is followed:

([the last name of the first author listed] *et al.*, [publish year])*

et al. is Latin for "and others"

 Exercise 10.3: Make it Right – Cite!

The Hulk needs to cite his source, which comes from the following reference:

Graham, R., Hannigan, L., Snavely, S., and Boylan, J.T. (2019). El Centro College BIOL 1406 Course Manual. Dallas, TX: El Centro College.

- What should be in the parentheses at the end of Hulk's paraphrased section?

> Matter is made up of atoms. The nucleus of an atom has protons with a positive charge and neutrons with a neutral charge. Electrons have a negative charge and are not in the nucleus. Electrons circle the nucleus in shells and because they have different levels of energy, the electrons are in different shells (,   ) .

Activity 10.4: Identifying Valid References

How do you find valid information for your papers in a science class? First, stick to the class materials as much as possible. Materials issued by the course instructor are, for the most part, valid references as textbooks have been peer-reviewed by groups of professionals and experts. Occasionally, your instructor may warn you about typos or provide updates if the book does not contain the latest scientific knowledge. Scientific books are another good source. Physical or digital copies can be found in the library. Articles written in well-known scientific journals are another option and these can be found using databases in the library.

But what about the internet? Students typically try to do the bulk of their research on the internet, as it is easy to search and contains a vast amount of information. Unfortunately, no one checks the facts on most of the websites. Many sites contain pseudo-scientific claims that are not backed by any evidence. Additionally, much of the information on websites is plagiarized from another source.

If you must conduct your research on the internet, it is best to stick to articles from well-known journals. Some can be found through sites like Google Scholar. But if you can only find the information you need on websites, be very careful. Try to ascertain who wrote the information and their credentials.

 Exercise 10.4: Using Websites for Research

You need to find references for your biology paper fast! You found information on four websites…

Website has an address of www.wikipedia.org
The information sounds good and there are tons of references. Authors are not listed. Anyone who has an account can write or edit any article.

Website has an address of https://irp.nih.gov
The information sounds good and there are links to many research articles. Content pages sometimes have an author listed.

Website has an address of https://scienceblog.com
The information seems accurate and while no authors are listed, scientists and their research are discussed in detail.

Website has an address of https://answers.yahoo.com
There are answers to many biology questions. Authors are not listed, but every answer have been rated by participants.

- Which website would be the most likely to contain valid information and why?

BIOL 1406 –Plagiarism and References

Pre-Lab Questions
1. Presenting another person's work as your own is
   a. paraphrasing.
   b. plagiarism.
   c. not wrong.

Post-Lab Questions
1. What is the problem with using quotes in a scientific paper?

2. Gamora has less than an hour to finish her paper for biology. She has found a good reference for the last section, but is having trouble paraphrasing everything because she doesn't understand some of the terms and there is no time to look them up. What should she do?

3. For Exercise 4, explain the potential problems with using material from each of the different websites as reference material.

Goals
1. Define and identify independent, dependent, and controlled variables.
2. Define and identify experimental versus control treatments.
3. Collect and analyze data under various experimental conditions.
4. Correctly support or reject your hypothesis based on the results of the experiment.

Activity 11.1: Enzyme Basics

Enzymes are complex organic molecules that act as biological catalysts to speed up the rates of chemical reactions. Without enzymes the chemical reactions required to maintain life would occur too slowly. Therefore, enzymes are essential to keep organisms alive. Enzymes temporarily bind to a specific **substrate**, also known as the reactant (or reactants) in a reaction. By physically bringing the reactants together, enzymes help to lower the amount of activation energy needed for the chemical reaction to occur.

In a reaction catalyzed by an enzyme, the substrate binds to the **active site**, which is a specific region of the enzyme that has an affinity for the substrate. The enzyme subsequently undergoes a conformational change to lock the substrate firmly into the active site, forming a temporary **enzyme-substrate complex**. Once the products of the reaction are formed, the enzyme-substrate complex ceases to exist and the enzyme changes back to its original shape (Figure 11.1).

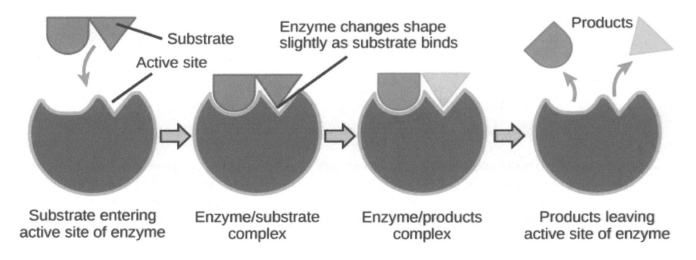

Substrate entering active site of enzyme — Enzyme/substrate complex — Enzyme/products complex — Products leaving active site of enzyme

Figure 11.1. Process of enzyme catalysis.

The vast majority of enzymes are large proteins composed of long chains of amino acids folded into a unique three-dimensional shape. As a result, the active site of each enzyme is specific to a certain substrate (this is referred to as **specificity**). After the chemical reaction occurs, the product has a different shape than the reactant(s) and no longer has the correct conformation to fit into the active site. Consequently, the enzyme releases the product and returns to its original shape. The enzyme is not used up or changed by the reaction and can catalyze additional reactions once its active site is empty.

For your scientific experiment, you will investigate the effects of temperature on enzyme activity. We will utilize the scientific method to determine how different temperatures affect the enzyme lactase, which catalyzes (speeds up) the decomposition of lactose into glucose and galactose.

 Exercise 11.1: Enzyme Recycling
What is the advantage of an enzyme being reusable?

Activity 11.2: Lactase Activity

The enzyme **lactase** is found in the small intestines of mammals to aid in the digestion of lactose. Lactose is a disaccharide composed of one glucose molecule and one galactose molecule bound together by a glycosidic bond. Lactose is the sugar found in dairy products such as milk and cheese. Mammals generally produce lactase in large amounts early in life when milk from the mother is the primary food source. As a young mammal develops and begins to eat a variety of foods, lactase levels in the body drop. Lactose-intolerance, a common digestive malady, is typically a by-product of the human body producing low levels of lactase.

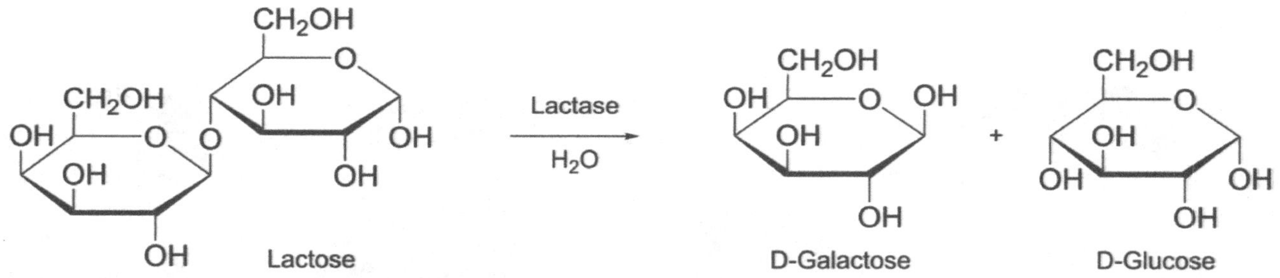

Figure 11.2. Lactose digestion into glucose and galactose aided by lactase.

Enzyme activity can either be measured by the amount of substrate used or by the amount of product produced. An experiment can be performed placing the enzyme and its substrate together and then measuring the expected product. Since glucose is a product of lactose digestion, the amount of glucose that is formed can be used as a measure of lactase activity in a given experiment.

 Exercise 11.2: Lactase Function
Per Figure 11.2, if five lactose molecules were in solution with five lactase molecules, how many glucose molecules would you expect to be produced? What about galactose?

Activity 11.3: Conducting an Experiment to Test Enzyme Activity

An **experiment** is an investigation conducted to test hypotheses. To do this, scientists design experiments so that changes to one variable cause another variable to change in a predictable way. A **variable** is any factor, trait, or condition that can exist in differing amounts or types. An experiment usually has three kinds of variables: independent, dependent, and controlled.

Designing experiments to test hypotheses requires considerable thought. The variables must be identified, appropriate measures developed, and influences outside of the experimental variables must be controlled. The **independent** variable will be varied during the experiment, while the **dependent** variable should change as a result. **Controlled** variables are also identified and maintained throughout the experiment. If kept constant, the controlled variables should not cause changes in the dependent variable. In some types of experiments, the goal is to investigate the effects of a substance or technique. The substance or technique is the independent variable but is usually referred to as an **experimental treatment**. For this type of experiment, it is necessary to also have a **control treatment**, in which the experimental treatment or treatments are removed. The control treatment, usually referred to as simply the "control", gives us a reference point so researchers can tell if the experimental treatments truly alter the dependent variable.

To better understand the different types of variables, let's examine the hypothesis that more sugar will dissolve in hot tea than cold tea. The independent variable in the experiment would be the temperature of the tea since it is being changed. The dependent variable is the amount of sugar that dissolves, which is influenced by the temperature of the tea. The controlled variables are kept constant and include the temperature in the room, tea type, amount of tea, amount of sugar, and sugar brand. Altering these variables could affect how much sugar dissolves at various temperatures. A way to identify the variables is to state the hypothesis as "Variable 1 is dependent upon variable 2." Variable 1 is the dependent variable and variable 2 is the independent variable. In our example, the amount of sugar that dissolves is dependent on the temperature of the tea.

Enzyme activity is affected by many factors, including temperature and pH. An enzyme will typically reach its highest activity level when at the optimum pH and temperature and activity will decrease above or below these points. For example, lipase is an enzyme produced by the pancreas to digest fats in the upper part of the small intestine. In humans the optimum pH is 8 and the optimum temperature is 37°C (98.6°F), which matches the conditions of the upper part of the small intestine.

Most enzymes function best within a certain range of environmental conditions. At low temperatures most molecules are moving too slowly for substrates to come into contact with enzymes, so enzyme activity is very low or nonexistent. At high temperatures or extreme pH values an enzyme may be **denatured** (inactivated due to loss of structure). High or low pH values alter the functional groups of amino acids and hydrogen bonds are easily disrupted at high temperatures. These changes, in turn, may disrupt the shape of the enzyme, reducing the affinity of the active site for its substrate. Changing the structure of a molecule changes its function. Therefore, it should not be surprising that denaturing an enzyme renders it inactive.

Exercise 11.3a: Testing Hypotheses and Identifying Variables

It is now time to generate and test hypotheses. As stated earlier, you will be investigating the effects of temperature on the activity of lactase using the scientific method. View the video of lactase activity at 0°C.

Observation:
There is essentially no lactase activity at 0°C, as no glucose (which is a product of the reaction) is measured.

Question:
What will occur to lactase activity at 37°C?

What will occur to lactase activity at 100°C?

Hypothesis:
Generate a hypothesis that relates to your question – it should be in the form of a statement. If your results support your hypothesis, you have greater certainty that your hypothesis is correct.

Prediction:
Based on your hypothesis predict the outcomes of lactase activity at 37°C and 100°C.

Variables:
For this experiment, identify the independent and dependent variables.

- Independent variable _____

- Dependent variable _____

Exercise 11.3b: Lactase activity at various temperatures

Materials needed: goggles, gloves, test tubes, test tube clamp, lactase solution, milk, hot plate, 250mL beaker, 100mL beaker, 10mL graduated cylinder, glucose test strips, water bath at 37°C, boiling chips, wax pencil

1. *Lactase at 0°C will be demonstrated by video or your instructor. Record results in Table 11.1.*
2. Start boiling water using the larger beaker, boiling chips, and the hot plate.
3. Obtain four test tubes. Mark the first test tube **37 L**, the second test tube **37 M**, the third test tube **100 L**, and the fourth test tube **100 M**.
4. Add 2 mL of lactase solution to the **37 L** and **100 L** test tubes.
5. Add 2 mL of milk to the **37 M** and **100 M** test tubes.
   - DO NOT add the lactase and milk to the same test tube.
6. Both test tubes labeled **37** should be placed in a 37°C water bath.
7. Both test tubes labeled **100** should be placed in the beaker of boiling water using a test tube clamp. Allow all test tubes to remain at their temperatures for <u>five minutes</u>.
8. After five minutes, carefully pour the contents of the **37 M** test tube into the **37 L** test tube and shake to mix, holding a gloved thumb over the top of the tube to shake thoroughly.
9. Return the **37** test tube (that now contains both milk and lactase) to the water bath. Allow it to remain at temperature for <u>ten minutes</u>.
10. Using the test tube clamp, remove the **100 M** and **100 L** test tubes from the boiling water and pour the contents of both tubes into the small beaker. Swirl to mix. Pour the contents of the beaker (containing both milk and lactase) into the **100 L** test tube and return the tube to the boiling water for <u>ten minutes</u>.
11. After ten minutes, remove the test tubes from the water bath and the boiling water.
12. Mix the tube from the water bath using a gloved thumb. When cool, do the same for the tube from the boiling water.
13. Using a pipette, add three drops of the **37** mixture to a glucose strip.
14. Wait 60 seconds and then immediately compare the color of the glucose indicator to the key provided. Record your results in Table 1.
15. Repeat steps 13 and 14 for the **100** test tube.
16. Record your results in Table 1. Collect data from all other teams in class and compute the average of all trials.

	0°C *demo*	37°C	100°C
Team 1			
Team 2			
Team 3			
Team 4			
Team 5			
Team 6			
AVERAGE			

Table 11.1. Glucose (in mg/dL) produced by lactose digestion aided by lactase.

Exercise 11.3c: Analysis & Conclusion

Data analysis is a crucial step of the scientific method. Scientists can obtain accurate data from an experiment only to misinterpret the results and have a flawed conclusion. Carefully examine the data for enzymatic activity at all temperatures.

- Which temperature was optimal for the activity of lactase?

- Did the results validate (support) or invalidate your hypothesis?

The data in Table 11.1 give how much glucose (in milligrams) each solution contained per deciliter of solution for each team. We calculate the average across all teams' trials in order to standardize the data. One trial of an experiment does not give enough data to validate/invalidate the experimental hypothesis. Experiments are typically performed multiple times to give researchers more confidence that their results are due to the independent variable and not due to chance. The process of averaging the data across several trials helps to eliminate outliers and strengthens the evidence for validating (or invalidating) the experimental hypothesis.

 Exercise 11.3d: Graphing the Data

Scientists frequently use graphs to view the data collected during an experiment.

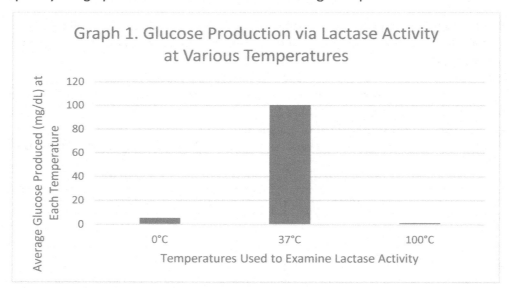

Graph 1. Results of the lactase experiment measuring glucose production at different temperatures.

- What is your conclusion on the effect of temperature on lactase activity?

- Which axis on Graph 1 represents the independent variable?

- Which axis on Graph 1 represents the dependent variable?

Checkpoint A

BIOL 1406 – Enzymes Questions

Pre-Lab Questions

1. Molecules that speed up the rates of chemical reactions are called:

   _____

2. Lactase digests lactose into:
   a. Glucose and Maltose
   b. Glucose and Galactose
   c. Glucose and Fructose

3. An enzyme will typically reach its highest activity level when at the _____ pH and temperature.

4. Lactase levels would be expected to be higher in younger mammals as compared to older mammals.
   a. True
   b. False

Post-Lab Questions

1. In the lactase experiment, explain how the independent variable affected the dependent variable and describe the importance of having a variety of temperatures.

2. Summarize how you used each of the seven steps of the scientific method to perform your experiment with lactase.

3. What mistakes were made during the lactase experiment and how might they have altered the results?

4. At what conclusion did you arrive based on your data? If you could perform the experiment again, what changes would you make to the experiment to allow for more accurate data?

Goals
1. Identify the sections of a scientific report.
2. Explain what type of information is included in each section of a scientific report.
3. Recognize well-written sections of a report by analyzing examples.

Activity 12.1: Scientific Reports

You may have heard the question "If a tree falls in a forest and no one is around to hear it, does it make a sound?" A similar question can be asked about experiments. "If a researcher performs an experiment and never publishes the result has science been performed?" Many people would say no because science is the accumulation of knowledge. If the results of an experiment are not published, knowledge is not gained. The final and very important step in the scientific process is to inform others of what you learned. Scientific reports have a specific format that is followed, with information organized into sections.

Abstract – This section is a brief summary of the entire lab report. It describes background information for the experiment, the purpose and hypothesis of the experiment, a summarized account of the procedure, abbreviated results, and a brief description of the conclusions made in the experiment.

Introduction – This sections is to provide all the background information necessary for your reader to understand your experiment. You should also describe why the experiment was done and the importance of it. Here, you explain what your hypothesis and predictions were.

Methods – This section describes what you did in enough detail that someone could repeat your experiment.

Results – What did you find out? This is where you present your data in both visual and verbal form.

Discussion – An explanation of your results. How does what you found relate to what others have found out? How do your results relate back to your original hypothesis and predicitions for the experiment.

References – This is a list of sources you used and cited in your paper.

 Exercise 12.1: Formatting

Why is it important for scientific reports to have a specific format?

The following exercises will help you distinguish good versus poor examples in a scientific report.

Activity 12.2: Before the Sections

Your audience should understand what the experiment was about from the **title**. Many times, readers only have the title of a paper to determine whether they want to read the report or not. If it is too general, it will not spark any interest in an audience. If it is too long, it will seem wordy.

 Exercise 12.2a: Title

A. Use of Various Sugars During Fermentation by Yeast (*Saccharomyces cerevisiae*)

B. Yeast Experiment

C. Production of Carbon Dioxide as a Measure of the Usefulness of Sucrose and Glucose as Food Sources for the Yeast (*Saccharomyces cerevisiae*) in Small Erlenmeyer Flasks

- Which of the above titles is the best? Why?

Abstracts are summaries and should concisely explain what the report contains. The abstract appears below the title of the report. Unlike a summary of a book that sometimes does not give away the ending, a scientific abstract tells the whole story. At the minimum, the abstract should have at least one sentence for each section (Introduction, Methods, Results, Discussion). This section should be written last.

 Exercise 12.2b: Abstract

A. Yeast (*Saccharomyces cerevisiae*) can use various sugars as food sources during fermentation. We tested the ability of yeast to use the monosaccharide glucose versus the disaccharide sucrose. The yeast produced carbon dioxide at an average rate of 10 ppm/minute when given glucose as a food source and 8 ppm/minute when given sucrose as a food source. Using carbon dioxide production, glucose was shown to be a better food source for yeast.

B. We tested which sugar is a better food source for yeast (*Saccharomyces cerevisiae*). Glucose is a six-carbon monosaccharide and sucrose is a disaccharide composed of glucose and fructose. During fermentation glucose is changed into ethanol and carbon dioxide. By measuring the amount of carbon dioxide produced we can determine which sugar is a better food source for the yeast. We used a sensor attached to the computer to measure carbon dioxide production for 10 minutes and then determine a rate of carbon dioxide.

- Which of the above abstracts is better? Why?

Activity 12.3: Introduction

Your **introduction** should start off with some general concepts about the subject area. If you are doing an experiment on sugar production during photosynthesis, you should concisely describe photosynthesis to your audience. (You must have in-text citations for every fact you present in the report, as verification of that fact's validity.) Then, explain the purpose of your experiment. Tell your audience what you expected to learn from the experiment. Finally, you need to state your hypothesis and prediction(s).

Remember, the hypothesis is the logical explanation of a scientific problem. The prediction is what should happen in your experiment if your hypothesis is correct. For example, you hypothesize a plant will undergo photosynthesis faster using blue light than green light. However, you cannot see photosynthesis directly happening. But you can measure the product of photosynthesis: sugars. Your prediction can be, if you placed a group of plants under green light and another group under blue light, then the plants under blue light would produce more sugars due to their higher rate of photosynthesis.

 Exercise 12.3: Introduction

A. Yeast are unicellular organisms that belong to the Kingdom Fungi and in an anaerobic environment (one without oxygen), they will produce ethanol and carbon dioxide as a byproduct of fermentation (Freeman, 2011). During the production of wine, yeast use the monosaccharide fructose as the reactant for fermentation (Freeman, 2011). But there are many different types of monosaccharides, glucose being the most widely used as an energy source by organisms (Freeman, 2011). We tested whether yeast could use other types of sugars for fermentation. We hypothesized yeast would ferment glucose more easily than other monosaccharides and if we tested glucose, fructose, and galactose, then glucose would result in the most rapid rate of carbon dioxide production.

B. We did this lab to learn how to do the scientific method. Yeast are small and make the alcohol in your wine. I think yeast are amazing organisms because they help us by making dough rise and of course they are really important because they produce the alcohol in beer and wine and western society would be very different if we did not have beer and wine to drink. So, the instructor made us test the yeast to see why they make different amounts of alcohol.

- In the above introductions put a box around the purpose, underline the hypothesis, and circle the prediction (if they have one).

- Of the two introductions, which is better? Why?

Activity 12.4: Methods

The **methods** should be the easiest section to write because it is the description of how you conducted the experiment. It should be detailed enough that someone else could repeat your experiment exactly as you performed it. This means they need to know specific details on your setup and equipment. Unlike a science fair project, the scientific report does NOT have a list of the materials that are used. Instead, you will introduce the materials when you describe your experiment. In addition to how you collected the data, this section needs to describe any calculations you performed to the data. For example, "to determine blood pressure we took the blood pressure in both the right and left arm and averaged the two measurements for each subject." And if you did not perform the exact procedure from the lab handout, you need to mention how the procedure was altered in this section. Methods are always written in the past tense.

 Exercise 12.4: Methods

A. Water was collected from White Rock Lake, Joe Pool Lake and Mountain Creek Lake.

B. Water samples were collected from White Rock Lake, Joe Pool Lake and Mountain Creek Lake. Each 500 ml sample was collected by slowly walking into the water to a depth of 0.5 m. A glass container was held under the water close to the surface until full and the lid was screwed on while the jar was still under water.

C. We collected 0.5 liter water samples from White Rock Lake, Joe Pool Lake and Mountain Creek Lake. For each sample, we used a glass jar that had markings to measure volume on the side. Before going into the water, we took off our shoes and rolled up our pants so they would not get wet. We walked into the water slowly until we reached a depth of 0.5 meter. We knew we had reached 0.5m because at that point the water was just touching our knee cap. We then unscrewed the top of the container and held it in our right hand while we held the jar under the water just below the surface with our left hand. Once, the jar was full of water we screwed on the lid while the jar was still under water. Then, we slowly walked out of the water and put our shoes back on.

- Underline any information that is not relevant.

- Which of the abbreviated methods above about collecting water for testing is better? Why?

Activity 12.5: Results

A scientific report can present **results** in three different ways: in the text, in a table, or in a figure. Data should be presented in a way that best conveys the overall results. For example, bar graphs are ideal when comparing averages between groups, but cannot show how measurements change over time as a line graph can. Present your data accurately—if your measurement was 20.8 cm, do not round up to 21 cm. As this section is all about measurements, make sure to include units for the measurements. "The snake was 20 long" does not give any real information. A 20 mm snake would look like a worm, a 20 cm snake would fit on this paper, but a 20 m snake is one for the record books.

Even if you present your data in charts and/or figures, you need to summarize trends in the data in the text of a paragraph. Trends are how the data changes, or fails to change, during the experiment - for example, "The heart rate increased from an average of 150 to 180 beats per minute when the mice were subjected to the epinephrine." However, you need to save any analysis of the data for the discussion section. And when referring to your charts and diagrams, DO NOT put "Table 1 shows the results of the experiment." Instead, you need to state what the results were, in general. For example, "The blood pressure of the treatment group was twenty-five percent higher than the control group (Table 1)."

 Exercise 12.5a: Tables and Figures

Is it acceptable to simply put a table or graph in the results section, but have no text in paragraph form? Why or why not?

Ways to present your data:

- Very simple data is usually given within the text.
"The average territory size of a male is 2.54 hectare but they can range from 0.33 to 5.18 hectares." This data does not need to be set off into a table.

- Some information is best presented in a table. Below is data from a student research project on begging behavior in flamingos.

Table 1. Begging bouts directed to each parent of a lesser flamingo chick.

Parent	**Unsuccessful Begs**	**Successful Begs**	**Total Begs**	**Success Rate**
Female	9	26	35	74%
Male	4	9	13	69%

Requirements and tips for tables:

- o Every table must have a title above it. The title should be detailed enough that a reader could understand the information without reading the text portion of the report.

- o The top row of the table must have headers for the columns and they should be bolded.

- o To help with readability, a table should have borders around each cell.

- o Tables are generally referred to parenthetically (i.e. in parentheses). An example for the above table: "Even though the chick begs more from the female parent, its success rate is similar for both parents (Table 1)."

- o Most student find tables easier to create in a word processing program (i.e. Microsoft Word) than in a spreadsheet (i.e. Excel).

- The last way to present data is in a figure. Figures are commonly used because it is easy to show complicated data in a figure.

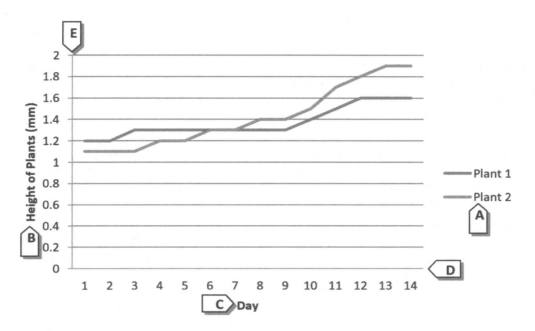

 Figure 1. Growth rate of two pinto bean (*Phaseolus vulgaris*) plants over 14 days.

Exercise 12.5b: Parts of a Figure
What letters point to the following parts of the graph?

X-axis	_____	Y-axis title	_____
X-axis title	_____	Legend	_____
Y-axis	_____	Figure title	_____

Requirements and tips for figures:

o Every figure must have a title. The title should be detailed enough that a reader could understand the information without reading the text portion of the report.

o Both axes must be labeled with units in parentheses. The independent variable is on the x-axis and the dependent variable is on the y-axis.

o Gridlines will help with readability.

o **NOT ALL CHARTS NEED LEGENDS**. You need a legend only if your points/bars use different symbols.

o Figures are generally referred to parenthetically. An example for the above figure: "Plant 2 had an initial height less than Plant 1, but grew at a faster rate (Figure 1)."

o Charts can be created in Excel or Word. Excel has free tutorials online. Producing charts is an essential skill so if you do not know how to do it, this is the time to learn!

Activity 12.6: Discussion

The **discussion** is normally the longest section of a paper and is usually the most difficult for students to write. The discussion should start off with a brief statement about your hypothesis and predictions, restating it to remind your audience. Then you want to state whether the results of your experiment supported or rejected your hypothesis. Clarity is important; you cannot accept one part and reject another part, as you would be implying the hypothesis is both right and wrong. If you feel tempted to use the word "prove" in this section, think about its scientific definition. Remember, rejecting a hypothesis is just as valid as supporting it. The discussion section is not an argument to convince the audience to accept your hypothesis; it is an analysis of the data to determine the truth.

You need to evaluate any inconsistencies in your data. If one reading is very high or very low compared to the others you collected, this may have skewed your averages to appear higher or lower than they should be. You need to explain why this error occurred and how it influenced your data overall. If you do not know the exact reason, you can use deductive reasoning to make an inference. For example, a group in your class might have treated their test organism with twice as many drops of alcohol as the instructions called for during the heart rate experiment, causing the results for the entire class to be biased. You don't know if this is the reason for the extremely low heart rate average, but it is a consequence and makes sense.

Relate your results to what has already been published, as this will help to serve as empirical evidence for why you accepted or supported your hypothesis. Perhaps your organism did not respond in the same fashion as seen in other experiments. If your results differed from what others obtained, you need to explain why. This can go into speculation and you can state your opinion, as you would most likely need to perform another experiment to be certain. However, your opinion must be a sound judgment, which is both coherent and logical.

Finally, based on the results you obtained, explain what you would do if you could conduct more experiments. What new hypothesis would you like to test?

Allow yourself plenty of time to write your discussion section, as analysis takes time.

Activity 12.7: References

Many students are confused about when and how to use citations and references. **Citations** are put in the text of your paper (usually parenthetically) and refer to publications in your References or Literature Cited section. **References** are detailed descriptions of the actual sources you used. For every citation in the paper you need a reference, and every reference should be cited in the paper. If you read an article but did not use any information for it in your report, it does NOT go in your Reference section.

Whenever you state a fact, you should put down how you know that fact. For example, if you were writing a paper on the effects of cocaine on *Daphnia magna* you might state in your introduction - Cocaine increases heart rates in humans (*Homo sapiens*) and dogs (*Canis familiaris*) (Kloner et al. 1992). In the Reference section of your paper you would have the following reference:

Kloner, R. A., Hale, S., Alker, K., & Rezkalla, S. (1992). The effects of acute and chronic cocaine use on the heart. *Circulation, 85,* 407-419.

Exercise 12.7a: When to Put in Citations

- Determine which of the statements below require citations.

    A. How the body responds to chemicals is very complicated.

    B. Caffeine increases heart rate in humans.

    C. Chimpanzees are the closest relatives of humans.

    D. Enrichment is necessary for the psychological wellbeing of primates.

    E. Climate change is a hotly debated topic.

Finding references. Scientific references are REQUIRED for a scientific report. It is easy to search for information on the internet. Unfortunately, no one checks the facts on most of the websites. Additionally, most of the information from websites is plagiarized from another source. The most credible references are articles that have been published in a well-known journal. These articles are reviewed by other scientists before they are published. Most scientific books are also credible sources. Unfortunately, access to these types of sources can be difficult to find at a community college. So, students frequently resort to doing a web search. This can be disastrous. Anyone can have a website and put whatever they want on it.

Where can you find scientific articles? Google scholar is only one avenue. You can search the databases of the college library. If you are not familiar with these databases, you need to learn to use them. The librarians are very happy to help. Encyclopedias are also a good starting point. They will usually have references for where they obtained their information.

References that should NOT be used in a scientific article are personal accounts, such as blogs or an individual's web page, and websites that end in .org or .com. Information on governmental (.gov) or educational (.edu) websites need to be used with caution. Does the website list where they obtained their information? Wikipedia is unfortunately NOT a credible website. However, it usually has references at the bottom of an article and some of those references may be credible. Please be aware that many may refer to other websites that are also not credible.

What about something that was found on Google books? These may be credible sources. Does the book include citations and references? If yes, then it is probably a good source. When you are listing this in your Reference section, you will list it as a book and not as a webpage.

Style of references. You will find a variety of styles if you look at the references of published papers. Every journal tends to have their own style. For this report (and most scientific papers you will write in college), you will use the APA style of formatting. DO NOT use the MLA style. Use https://owl.purdue.edu/owl/research_and_citation/apa_style/apa_style_introduction.html for detailed instructions. References must be alphabetized and they should have a hanging indent, meaning that the second line is indented.

Exercise 12.7b: Reference Style

- Using the website above, determine which of these references are in the correct APA style.

"Ho Chi Minh." Encyclopaedia Britannica. 2003. Britannica.com. 15 May 2003
    <http://www.britannica.com>.

Anderson, A. K., Christoff, K., Panitz, D., De Rosa, E., & Gabrieli, J. D. E. (2003). Neural correlates of the
    automatic processing of threat facial signals. *Journal of Neuroscience*, 23, 5627–5633.

Bell, Stewart. The Martyr's Oath: The Apprenticeship of a Homegrown Terrorist. Mississauga, ON: Wiley,
    2005.

Heuristic. (n.d.). In Merriam-Webster's online dictionary (11th ed.). Retrieved from http://www.m-
    w.com/dictionary/heuristic

Activity 12.8: Which Section is What?

As you have learned, it is very important to put the correct information in each section of your scientific report. If someone reads a report and wants to look at the data obtained from the experiment in detail, they will go directly to the results section. It would be very confusing to find that data in a different section.

Exercise 12.8: Sections of a lab report

In what section of a scientific report would you find the following statements?

_____Introduction   _____Methods   _____Results   _____Discussion

1. Analysis for methylmercury was conducted by Flett Research Ltd. (Winnipeg, MB). Approximately 0.3 g of blood-anticoagulant mixture was analyzed by KBr extraction, followed by ethylation, purge and trap and cold vapor atomic fluorescence spectroscopy (CVAFS). The analysis batch included a procedural blank and a reference sample (DORM-2, National Research Council of Canada).

2. All adults have measurable quantities of pesticides and other toxins in their blood. We examined whether newborn babies were born with measurable quantities of pesticides in their blood and expected that the level of pesticides in newborn blood would be related to the amount found in their mothers.

3. Our study found PFOA (Ingredient in Teflon) in all 10 newborns tested. This is similar to a study by the EPA that found PFOA in more than 95 percent of Americans.

4. Alpha-Chlordane was found in 9 of 10 umbilical cord blood samples from babies born in U.S. hospitals in 2004, at concentrations ranging from 25.1 to 371.9 pg/g (lipid weight, in whole blood).

Checkpoint A

BIOL 1406 – Scientific Reports Questions

Pre-Lab Questions

1. What is a summary of a report called?

   _____

2. As part of the scientific method, scientists must publish the discoveries they make in the course of performing experiments so that everyone has access to the knowledge gained.
   a. True
   b. False

3. Where would you find an analysis of the data in a scientific report?
   a. Methods
   b. Results
   c. Discussion

4. What word should you avoid using in a scientific report, because your results may not be typical in every situation?

   _____

Post-Lab Questions

1. Why is the abstract an important part of a scientific paper?

2. How should you write you methods section compared to instructions that you would follow in the lab handout?

3. How do the results section differ from the discussion section?

Supplemental Information for Lab Report sections

General Information for **your** Scientific Report Sections

Not following the information below will result in deductions on your lab report sections.

1. When you conducted the experiments, you did so in a group. And you collected data from the entire class. However, the lab report is **NOT** a group activity. You need to turn in your own work.
2. Plagiarism is the copying of another student's work, copying information from a book, or copying information found on a website. YOU are the author of this paper so all of the words need to be yours, not someone else's. Yes, it is tempting when someone else has written something so eloquently, but you know SafeAssign will find you out!
3. No quotes! You need to define words and explain concepts in your own words.
4. It must be double-spaced using 12-point Arial font in text and tables. Figures must use Arial.
5. There is not a magic number of words or number of pages. Keep your paper as short as possible. You will not receive a better grade for a longer paper. However, you need to explain everything adequately.
6. This is not a composition paper. Papers you write for English courses are filled with your personal opinions. This is not an English course. Technical writing demands a clear, concise explanation of the facts. Your report needs to contain only facts regarding the experiment.
7. When you refer to a species in the paper, you must give the complete scientific name in the proper format the first time. For example, if you are experimenting on humans, you would state that the research was performed on *Homo sapiens*. If you use multiple species from a certain genus, you will simply use the genus name (i.e. *Homo*, if discussing different species of humans.)
8. The experiment is in the past, so any part of your paper that relates to it must be in the past tense. Facts found in other published papers are written in the present. For example, *Daphnia magna* **have** a clearly visible heart (Graham et al., 2017). We **tested** the effects of chemicals on heart rate.
9. You will be writing the introduction, methods, results, discussion, and reference sections for practice, but you will not turn in a complete lab report. Instead, you will evaluate a complete lab report near the end of the semester.
10. You will be writing more papers in the future so learning good technique now is important.

Format Template for a Lab Report

The next page shows how, in general, a report needs to be formatted and contains important information that should be included to receive the highest score. Be sure to write down any specifics your lab instructor gives you in class.

Descriptive Title

Your name

Scientific Reports - 104

This is the abstract. It is indented one inch on both sides to set it apart from the rest of the paper. It is a summary of your paper and is usually written last. It will be easier to pull the most important bits from your sections if you write everything else first. Be sure to include the purpose, the basic methods of the experiment, the general results, and a brief discussion. Make sure it is no more than 5 or 6 sentences long.

Introduction

Introduce the basic concepts of the experiment in this section. What background information will you need to give the reader so that they will understand the experiment(s)? What is the purpose of the experiment – why did you do it? While your instructor will be reading and grading these reports, you should be writing for an audience that does not have basic knowledge of cellular biology and has not performed this experiment. Reference sources within your paper by using the last name and date in parentheses at the end of the sentence (Graham et al., 2017). Everything must be in your own words, as writing down someone else's words is plagiarism. Do not forget your hypothesis and prediction. Note: this one paragraph explaining what should be in your introduction is **not** indicative of how long your introduction should be!

Methods

In paragraph form, how did you perform the experiment? Summarize the procedure from your lab book, do not copy everything. The steps you performed should not be numbered like in the lab manual. You should not have a list of materials at the beginning. Your group only performed a single experiment, but you still need to summarize all the experiments performed by your class. Just be sure to state which experiments your group actually performed. This is <u>not</u> the section to report your results. This section must be written in past tense.

Results

In this section you need to tell your audience what happened during the experiment using tables and graphs. All tables/graphs need to be embedded in the Results section, <u>NOT</u> on a separate piece of paper. Discuss trends, but do not explain why you obtained the results you did – that is for the next section. For example, "Below are the results for the different predator and prey population sizes. Organism A's population size decreased whiles Organism B's populations increased (Table 1)". Be sure to label and number your tables/graphs and refer to them in your text.

Discussion

This section is an analysis of the results. Did you accept or reject your hypothesis? On what basis did you accept or reject your hypothesis. Were your results similar to other groups in the class? Did you compare your results to those for the class and discuss the similarities and/or differences? Were your results similar to what others have published? (Refer to specific published data as evidence.) What were the results for the drug you did not test? What is the physiological explanation for how various salinity levels affected your organism? (Again, refer to published material as evidence.) Use the correct terminology in regards to the scientific method, experiments, and biology. If there were any mistakes made during the experiments, how did this affect your results and were you able to correct them? And if you were able to do another experiment based on what your learned from this experiment, what hypothesis would you like to test?

References

You need at least one reference other than your textbook and the lab handout, for a minimum of three.   Use APA formatting. (The example below shows the lab handout in APA format.)

Graham, R., Hannigan, L., Snavely, S., and Boylan, J.T. (2019). El Centro College BIOL 1406 Course Manual. Dallas, TX: El Centro College.

Goals
1. Explain oxidation-reduction reactions.
2. Define glycolysis and cellular respiration.
3. Write the chemical equation for cellular respiration.
4. Explain the formation of carbonic acid.
5. Perform experiments to determine carbon dioxide production of different organisms.

Activity 13.1: The Efficiency of Respiration

Millions of chemical reactions are occurring in your cells every second. During chemical reactions the electrons of atoms are rearranged. In some reactions, one atom will lose an electron and another will gain an electron. These reactions are identified as oxidation-reduction (redox) reactions. The atom that is **oxidized** loses an electron and the atom that gains an electron is **reduced**. One way to remember this is "LEO goes GER" (Lose Electron = Oxidation, Gain Electron = Reduction). For example, in the equation Na + Cl $\rightarrow$ Na$^+$Cl$^-$, Na loses an electron and is oxidized, while Cl gains an electron and is reduced.

In some reactions, an atom may not lose total possession of electrons. An atom's ability to lose or gain electrons is based on its affinity for electrons – its **electronegativity**. Consider O_2 and H_2O. Within an O_2 molecule, the electrons occupy each atom's orbital for an equal amount of time. This occurs because each oxygen atom has the same electronegativity. However, in a water molecule the electrons spend more time around the oxygen atom. This unequal sharing is a result of the weak electronegativity of hydrogen and as a result, the electrons spend less time around the hydrogen atoms and more time around the oxygen atom. Therefore, oxygen has "gained" electrons, while the hydrogen atoms have "lost" electrons. Thus, for the reaction $2H_2 + O_2 \rightarrow 2H_2O$, H_2 is oxidized and O_2 is reduced.

Life is maintained by redox reactions. All organisms must have a continual supply of external energy in order to maintain life. During photosynthesis, plants capture light energy and convert it to the chemical energy of carbohydrates. To fuel metabolic processes, both autotrophs and heterotrophs must break down the sugars produced by photosynthesis to utilize the stored energy. **Metabolism** consists of chemical reactions catalyzed by enzymes that allow organisms to grow and reproduce, respond to their environments, and maintain their structures. These metabolic processes might be catabolic or anabolic. **Catabolism** involves the breakdown of large molecules into smaller molecules, while **anabolism** builds complex molecules from simpler subunits. The general equation for cellular respiration is:

$$C_6H_{12}O_6 + 6O_2 \longrightarrow 6CO_2 + 6H_2O$$

In this reaction the carbon in glucose is oxidized and the oxygen in O_2 is reduced. When the chemical bonds in carbohydrates are broken, the released energy is captured by high-energy phosphate bonds by combining inorganic phosphate (P_i) with adenosine diphosphate (ADP) to form adenosine triphosphate (ATP). **ATP** is an energy-storage molecule utilized to power chemical reactions in the cell. During cellular respiration, many molecules of ATP can be produced for each glucose molecule. In the past, scientists calculated that 36-38 ATP molecules could be produced during cellular respiration but current research places the total closer to 29-32 ATP molecules.

Exercise 13.1: Cellular respiration   *Lecture*

- Rewrite the equation for cellular respiration adding in P_i, ADP and ATP.

Activity 13.2: Glucose Metabolism

The first step of glucose metabolism is **glycolysis**, in which a six-carbon glucose molecule is split in two. When this occurs, two molecules of **pyruvate** (each containing three carbons) are produced. In addition, the breakdown of glucose releases energy that is transferred to high-energy bonds connecting inorganic phosphate (P_i) to ADP molecules. This results in the net production of 2 ATP molecules. In addition, NAD^+ is reduced to create two electron-carrying molecules of **NADH**.

Glycolysis can occur with or without oxygen. In the presence of oxygen (the typical state), glycolysis is the first stage of cellular respiration. Without oxygen, fermentation follows glycolysis and allows cells to make small amounts of ATP.

Exercise 13.2a: Glycolysis   *Lecture*

- Write a chemical equation for glycolysis.

Exercise 13.2b: Oxygen and Glucose Breakdown   *Lecture*

- What occurs after glycolysis if oxygen is not present in the cell? What if oxygen is present?

 **Exercise 13.2c: The fate of pyruvate**   *Lecture*

If oxygen is present, what happens to pyruvate? In groups, model out the complete oxidation of pyruvate.

Exercise 13.2d: ATP Production   *Lecture*

Even after pyruvate is completely catabolized, the majority of the ATP molecules have not yet been produced. How are most of the ATP molecules produced in cellular (aerobic) respiration?

Activity 13.3: Carbon Dioxide Production by Humans

As carbon dioxide is a product of cellular respiration, it can be used as evidence that cellular respiration is occurring. Because it is a gas, carbon dioxide can be difficult to collect. However, carbon dioxide easily dissolves in water and produces **carbonic acid** (H_2CO_3), as indicated by the following chemical equation:

$$CO_2 \; + \; H_2O \longrightarrow H_2CO_3$$

As an acid, carbonic acid lowers the pH of a solution by releasing hydrogen ions (H+). Therefore, if the carbon dioxide of an organism undergoing cellular respiration dissolves in water, the pH of the water will decrease as a result of carbonic acid production. To easily detect the pH reduction, an indicator called bromothymol blue can be used. **Bromothymol blue** turns from blue to green to yellow in increasingly acidic conditions.

In the following exercise, you will determine whether the respiratory gases produced by humans have more carbon dioxide compared to atmospheric air.

 Exercise 13.3: Human Respiration

Materials needed: bromothymol blue, straws, test tubes, rubber bulb, china marker, graduated cylinder, safety glasses
1. Obtain 2 test tubes and mark the tubes 1 & 2.
2. Add 3 mL of water to each test tube.
3. Add 3 drops of bromothymol blue to each tube.
4. Record the initial color of the solution in Table 13.1.
5. Attach a straw to the bulb and pump air into the solution of test tube 1 for 2 minutes.
6. Put on safety goggles, insert a straw into test tube 2, and use it to *gently* blow exhaled air into the solution of test tube 2 for 2 minutes.
7. Record the final color of the solutions in Table 13.1 and note whether there was an increase in acidity resulting from an increase in carbonic acid.
8. Dispose of the straw and test tubes in the biohazard container.

Table 13.1. Carbon Dioxide Production in Humans

Tube	Treatment	Initial Color	Final Color	CO_2 Change
1				
2				

- What is the purpose of Tube 1?

Checkpoint A

Activity 13.4: Carbon Dioxide Production in Plants and Animals

You have determined humans undergo cellular respiration and produce carbon dioxide, but what about other animals? Or plants? In the next exercise, you will investigate the rate of carbon dioxide (CO_2) produced by different types of organisms, specifically beetle larvae and germinating seeds.

- Complete the hypothesis: _____ is dependent upon _____

- What are the independent and dependent variables in this experiment?

- What is your prediction?

 Exercise 13.4: Plant and Animal Respiration

Materials needed: bromothymol blue, 3 test tubes, 4 germinating pea seeds, 8 beetle larvae (or adult beetles), 3 small gauze squares, glass beads, 3 cotton balls, tweezers, corks

1. Obtain 3 test tubes and mark the tubes 3, 4, & 5.
2. Add 5 drops of bromothymol blue to each tube.
3. Record the initial color of the solution in Table 13.1.
4. Place enough glass beads into each test tube so that the larvae and seeds can rest on top of the beads and remain out of the solution.
5. Place a single, folded piece of gauze on top of the glass beads using tweezers.
6. Add 8-10 glass beads on top of gauze.
7. Place four (4) germinating pea seeds in test tube 3, eight (8) beetle larvae in test tube 4, and nothing in test tube 5.
8. Insert a cotton ball into the top of each of the three test tubes and push down to the center of the test tube using tweezers.
9. Insert a cork into the top of each test tube.
10. Place the test tubes in the test tube rack and wait at least 12 minutes.
11. Record the final color of the solutions in Table 13.1. Note if there was an <u>increase</u> in carbon dioxide concentration or <u>no increase</u>.

Table 13.1: Carbon Dioxide Production in Animals and Plants

Tube	Initial Color	Final Color	CO_2 Change
3			
4			
5			

- Is there a difference in the final colors for test tubes 3, 4 & 5? Why or why not? Compare your results with other groups.

- Based on your results, should you reject or accept your initial hypothesis? Why?

BIOL 1406 – Cellular Respiration Questions

Pre-Lab Questions

1. Redox reactions involve the loss and gain of
   a. Electrons
   b. Neutrons
   c. Carbon

2. When glucose is metabolized (broken down), the energy released is eventually transferred to which molecule?

   _____

3. During cellular respiration, in what form do the carbon atoms removed from glucose escape as?

   _____

4. When carbon dioxide dissolves in water, what does it turn into?
   a. Hydrochloric acid
   b. Pyruvate
   c. Carbonic acid

Post-Lab Questions

1. Explain how the carbon in glucose "loses" electrons and how the oxygen in O_2 "gains" electrons.

2. In our experiment, time is a controlled variable. How does a controlled variable differ from the independent and dependent variables?

3. Why was it necessary to have controls in the experiments?

4. Why was bromothymol blue used to indicate the production of carbon dioxide?

5. Why were germinating peas used in Activity 13.4 and not plants with green leaves?

6. Is there a difference in the amount of CO_2 produced for the different treatments of Activity 13.4? Why or why not? Compare your results with other groups.

7. If you could run this experiment again, which organisms might you add and why?

Goals
1. Distinguish the difference between scientific technical writing and other written forms.
2. Recognize complete sentences from sentence fragments.
3. Identify proper grammar and sentence structure.

Activity 14.1: Scientific Writing

At this point in your academic career, you've likely had to complete many different writing assignments. From book reports to poems to thesis statements and five paragraph essays, you've got some writing experience. Well guess what? You're going to be writing in this class too! A significant portion of your semester grade will come from your lab report. A **lab report** is a scientific paper designed to deliver technical details and data. As such, you may not have ever written anything like a lab report before.

While English assignments are designed to be creative, argumentative, and/or persuasive, scientific and technical writing assignments are not. Typically, these are "just the facts" reports which contain scientific facts and terminology without flowery or catchy language. Scientific writing is not meant to 'draw the reader in'; the readers of scientific papers go looking for them to find specific information (usually via a database like the ones we can use through our library).

Exercise 14.1: Scientific Writing versus Literary Writing
Examine the writing samples below. Which of the two represents appropriate scientific writing? Which represents inappropriate language for scientific papers?

A. Members of Kingdom Plantae are capable of photosynthesis, the process of converting sunlight into chemical energy (sugars). This important biological reaction uses water and atmospheric carbon dioxide to produce glucose and oxygen. Most life on earth is dependent upon this process; animals, fungi, protists, and many bacteria rely on the sugars made by photosynthesizers.

B. Plants are really cool! They take sunlight and make it into food! Plants make it possible for animals like you and me to exist because they make food for all of us. We would not be here without plants. Hug a tree today!

*   Which sample uses language which is inappropriate for scientific writing? _____

*   What aspects of this sample are inappropriate for scientific writing?

Activity 14.2: Vague versus Specific

Sometimes it can be difficult to explain exactly what we mean in written form. Often this is because we know what we mean in our heads, but fail to communicate this in writing. One way to minimize confusing the reader is to limit the use of pronouns (it, they, them, etc.).

 Exercise 14.2a: Pronouns and Vague Writing

Examine the writing samples below. Which of the two is clear and specific? Which is confusing and unclear?

A. The light reactions of photosynthesis take place when light is present. The dark reactions of photosynthesis can take place whether or not light is present. For this reason the light reactions are called the 'light-dependent reactions', while the dark reactions are called the 'light-independent reactions'.

B. Some reactions are called light reactions because they need it. When it is there they can use it. When it is dark the dark reactions can happen because they don't need it. Light-dependent reactions need it while dark reactions don't.

- Which sample uses language which is inappropriate for scientific writing? _____

- What aspects of this sample are inappropriate for scientific writing?

 Exercise 14.2b: More Pronouns and Vague Writing

Examine the writing samples below. Which of the two is clear and specific? Which is confusing and unclear?

A. We are surrounded by plants every day. Even when you don't notice them, they are using photosynthesis to convert sunlight into energy. It is an abundant source of energy for the world. Without it everything would die. That is how important it is.

B. The process of photosynthesis provides energy for plants as well as other organisms such as animals and fungi. The chlorophyll contained within plants captures light energy to use in building sugars from carbon dioxide. The sugars are broken down in the mitochondria to release this energy.

- Which sample uses language which is inappropriate for scientific writing? _____

- What aspects of this sample are inappropriate for scientific writing?

Activity 14.3: Grammar

Poor grammar can ruin an otherwise quality paper. While this is not an English class, this is a college-level biology class, and your writing should be college-level as well. Tense changes, sentence fragments, and run-on sentences are just a few examples of grammatical issues that can destroy your writing. A good-quality paper will keep grammatical errors to a minimum in order to increase clarity and comprehension of the overall topic.

 Exercise 14.3a: General Grammar

Examine the writing samples below. Which of the two represents appropriate scientific writing? Which represents inappropriate language for scientific papers?

   A. The light-reactions of photosynthesis happen in the day. When there is light. Energy is taken from the suns and used to make sugar. These then are used by a plant to be able to do it's processes. The dark reactions do not need lights energy so they can happen at night or during the day because light is not important here and called light independent.

   B. The light reactions of photosynthesis occur during the daylight hours. Light energy is absorbed by chlorophyll during the light reactions. This energy is then used to synthesize sugar during the dark reactions. The dark reactions can occur with or without sunlight. The sugars made during the dark reactions can then be used by the plant for energy.

   • Which sample uses language which is inappropriate for scientific writing? _____

   • What aspects of this sample are inappropriate for scientific writing?

 Exercise 14.3b: Subject/Verb Agreement

Examine the writing samples below. Circle the correct verb in each sentence such that all sentences are grammatically correct.

   • The plants on the shelf (was, were) dead.

   • The plants in the maze (were, was) hidden.

   • The plant with the leaves (is, are) pretty.

   • Bamboo and clover (belong, belongs) in the plant kingdom.

Compare your answers with your lab partner(s). Do you agree?

Exercise 14.3c: Sentence Fragments

All sentences must contain three things: a subject, a verb, and a complete thought. Examine the writing samples below. Which represent complete sentences?

- The plants are dead.

- The plants in the maze.

- The plant is pretty.

- Belonging in the plant kingdom.

Compare your answers with your lab partner(s). Do you agree?

 Exercise 14.3d: Run-on Sentences

In scientific and technical writing, being concise is preferred over being wordy. Examine the writing samples below. Which represent correct and concise sentences?

- The plants are dead, we should have a funeral.

- The plants in the maze are green.

- Plant cells need light to perform the light reactions, they are the light-dependent reactions.

- Photosynthesis is necessary for most life on Earth.

Compare your answers with your lab partner(s). Do you agree? What could you do to the run-on sentences above to correct the sentence structure?

Activity 14.5: Writing Resources

Read up on strategies for writing an academic paper.
- http://owl.english.purdue.edu/owl/section/1/2/

Know your grammar and punctuation rules.
- Comma usage: https://writingcenter.unc.edu/tips-and-tools/commas/
- Subject-Verb agreement: https://writingcenter.unc.edu/tips-and-tools/verb-tenses/
- Run-ons and fragments: http://writingcenter.unc.edu/handouts/fragments-and-run-ons/

Check out the Dallas College Tutoring website for more resources.
- https://www.dallascollege.edu/resources/tutoring/pages/default.aspx
- Dallas College Tutoring Services are a great resource; however, do no wait until the last minute to try to schedule time with a tutor! The closer we get to the end of the semester, the busier they get!

BIOL 1406 – Writing Questions

Pre-Lab Questions
1. Quality scientific writing should be:
   a. Clear
   b. Concise
   c. Grammatically correct
   d. All of the above

2. Your lab report assignment is worth _____ points.

3. You should proofread all of your work to help minimize errors.
   a. True
   b. False

Post-Lab Questions
1. Why is it important to use specific (not vague) language in a technical report?

2. Why is it important to use proper grammar and sentence structure in a report?

3. Compare and contrast scientific/technical writing and literary/creative writing.

EL CENTRO CAMPUS BIOL 1406 PBL
Photosynthesis

Goals
1. Identify the reactants and products for photosynthesis for both the light reactions and the Calvin Cycle.
2. Identify and explain the function of leaf structures.
3. Explain the process of paper chromatography.
4. Separate and identify photosynthetic pigments.
5. Explain the importance of starch and how it is formed.
6. Determine experimentally the role of chlorophyll in photosynthesis.

Activity 15.1: Products of Photosynthesis

Photosynthesis utilizes light energy to produce organic molecules. It is believed to be the single most important biological process, as most organisms would not be able to survive without its products. Photosynthesis involves two different sets of chemical reactions, the light reactions (light-dependent) and the Calvin cycle (light-independent). In the **light reactions**, light energy is captured by pigment molecules and transferred to energy-carrying molecules. This involves the loss of electrons from the pigment molecules, which are replenished by the hydrolysis of water (H_2O) with oxygen (O_2) released as a byproduct. In the **Calvin Cycle**, the energy-carrying molecules are used to convert carbon dioxide (CO_2) into glucose ($C_6H_{12}O_6$). The following equation summarizes photosynthesis:

$$6CO_2 + 6H_2O \xrightarrow{\text{light energy}} C_6H_{12}O_6 + 6O_2$$

Plants, as well as some protists and bacteria, are capable of photosynthesis. These photosynthetic organisms are **autotrophs** because they can synthesize organic compounds from carbon dioxide. **Heterotrophs,** such as animals, must obtain their nutrients by consuming autotrophs, either directly or indirectly.

 Exercise 15.1: The Food Chain   *Lecture*
- How is a lion dependent upon photosynthesis?

Activity 15.2: Leaf Anatomy

Leaves are the primary sites of photosynthesis in plants (Figure 15.1). The **epidermis**, composed of a layer of cells, covers the upper and lower surface of the leaf. A waxy **cuticle** on the epidermis helps to prevent water loss. **Stomata** consisting of a pore in the epidermis layer surrounded by **guard cells** permit the exchange of gases, such as oxygen and carbon dioxide. **Mesophyll cells** are found in the interior of the leaf and contain large amounts of chloroplasts, which are the organelles of photosynthesis. A double plasma membrane surrounds the interior of the chloroplast, the **stroma**. Within the stroma are flattened sacs called **thylakoids** arranged in stacks of **grana**.

Exercise 15.2a: Leaf Anatomy Model

Look at the model of a cross section of a leaf. On the picture below, identify the stoma pore and guard cell, mesophyll cells, chloroplasts, epidermis, and cuticle.

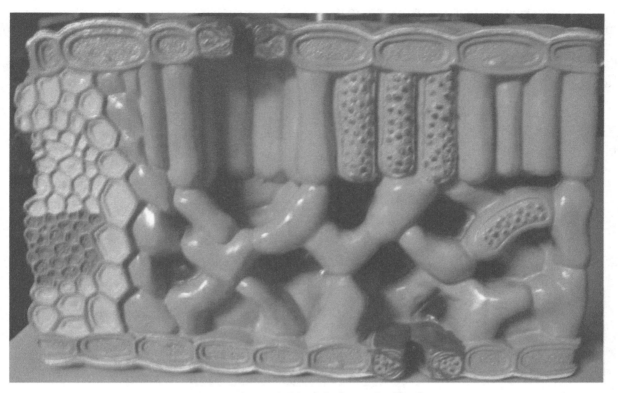

Figure 1. Model of a typical leaf.

 Exercise 15.2b: Leaf Anatomy

Look at the slide of *Ligustrum* leaf under the microscope and identify the different cell types. Find the mesophyll cells with their chloroplasts. Draw the leaf below and label the different types of cells and the stomata.

Activity 15.3: Photosynthetic Pigments

The green color of plants is due to light-absorbing molecules of the pigment **chlorophyll** embedded within the thylakoid membrane. A **pigment** is a substance with molecules that absorb, reflect, or transmit different wavelengths of light. Light wavelengths correspond to different energy levels, ranging from violet with a high-energy wavelength about 400 nm to red with a low-energy wavelength about 700 nm. Some pigments transmit light and appear transparent. On the other hand, a pigment appears black if it absorbs all wavelengths of visible light and appears white if it reflects all light wavelengths. Pigments of other colors will absorb and reflect one or more light wavelengths. Green pigments, for example, reflect wavelengths in the green portion of the visible light spectrum.

The chlorophyll in plants exists in two forms designated *a* and *b*. Both pigments absorb light in the red, blue, and violet wavelengths (Figure 2). Orange **carotenes** and yellow **xanthophylls** act as accessory pigments to chlorophyll.

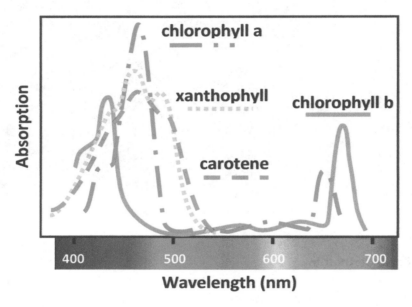

Figure 15.2. Absorption spectrums of pigments found in spinach leaves.

✎ **Exercise 15.3a: Pigments and Absorption of Light**   *Lecture*

• In Figure 15.2, the y-axis indicates the amount of light absorbed. What does the x-axis indicate?

• What do the four different lines on the graph show?

- What is the highest energy of visible light?

- At what wavelength does chlorophyll b have the highest absorption?

- As the absorption level drops, what is happening to the light?

- Based on the graph, which pigment should be a blue-green color?

- Based on the graph, which pigment should be a yellow-green color?

To determine the pigments found in photosynthetic organisms, you will separate the pigments using a technique called **paper chromatography**. The pigment mixture is applied to a paper with polar properties, which is placed into a mostly nonpolar solvent. As the solvent moves up the paper, it carries the dissolved pigments. The distance moved by the pigments depends upon their solubility in the solvent versus their affinity for the paper. The most polar substance has a greater affinity for the chromatography paper and will move the least, while the least polar substance (the most soluble) will travel the farthest.

Exercise 15.3b: Separating Pigments with Paper Chromatography

Materials needed: chromatography paper, developing solvent, spinach, quarter, chromatography tube and stopper, scissors, large beaker rack, metric ruler, goggles, gloves

1. Obtain a strip of chromatography paper. Hold by the edges, as the oil from your fingers will contaminate the paper.
2. With a pencil, lightly mark across the strip about 2 cm from the end.
3. Place a piece of spinach leaf under the pencil line.
4. Using the edge of a quarter, roll and press the spinach across the strip to deposit the pigments (Figure 15.3). Repeat 10-15 times. The goal is to produce a tight, dark line of pigment.

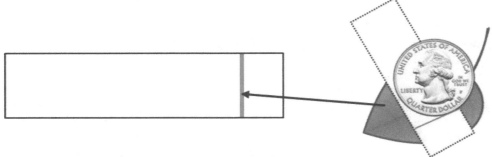

Figure 15.3. Application of spinach pigments on prepared chromatography paper.

5. After your instructor adds solvent into the chromatography tube (Figure 15.4), insert the strip into the tube and secure the stopper. **DO NOT LET THE PIGMENT LINE TOUCH THE SOLVENT**.
6. Place chromatography tube in the test tube rack and wait approximately 10-15 minutes. Your instructor may ask you to begin working on the next exercise during this time.
7. When solvent is 2 cm from the top, remove strip and allow to air-dry on a paper towel.
8. On the diagram of the chromatography strip below, draw and label how the different pigments separated. Identify the pigments by their colors. Label the strip with the pigment names.
9. Pour solvent into organic waste container and allow chromatography tube to air-dry without stopper. Do not rinse with water.

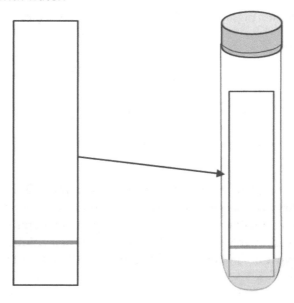

Figure 15.4. Setup of equipment for chromatography

- Which pigment is the most polar (least soluble), which is the least polar (most soluble)?

- What would have happened if the solvent in the chromatography tube covered the pigment line on the chromatography strip?

Checkpoint A

Activity 15.4: Requirements for Photosynthesis

One of the products of photosynthesis is sugar in the form of glucose ($C_6H_{12}O_6$). Plant use carbon dioxide to synthesize glucose through a series of chemical reactions called the Calvin (or C_3) cycle, which occurs within the stroma of the chloroplasts. The glucose is used to fuel cellular respiration and much is transported out of the chloroplast to other cells in the plant. The glucose that remains in the photosynthetic cells is combined with other glucose molecules to produce the polysaccharide **starch** and is stored until needed.

In the following exercises you will investigate requirements needed for photosynthesis to occur. You will indirectly determine photosynthetic activity by testing for the presence of starch using Lugol's solution [iodine potassium iodide (I_2KI)], which stains starch purple-black.

To determine whether chlorophyll is necessary for photosynthesis to occur, you will use the leaves of the *Coleus* plant. Horticulturalists have developed a variety of the *Coleus* plant that is **variegated**, meaning some areas of the leaves are green and some are white. The white areas do not contain chlorophyll.

- If chlorophyll is necessary for photosynthesis, which areas on the leaf should produce starch?

Exercise 15.4: Chloroplasts and Photosynthesis

Materials needed: Coleus *leaf, 100-mL beaker; 250-mL beaker, hot plate, boiling chips, ethanol or isopropyl alcohol, Petri dish, iodine (Lugol's IKI), forceps, beaker tongs, goggles, gloves*

1. Obtain one of the leaves from the *Coleus* plant and **outline it below**. Draw lines to indicate the portion that is green and the portion that is white.

Sketch of *Coleus* leaf

2. Hold the leaf with forceps and drop it into a 250-mL beaker half-full of boiling water (with boiling chips) for 3-5 minutes to rupture the cells.
   - Do not boil for too long or you will have mush. (This breaks down the cellulose in the cell walls so that the ethanol can get into the cells and destroy chlorophyll and other pigments.)
3. Fill a 100-mL beaker 1/3 full of ethanol and add a couple of boiling chips.
4. Transfer the leaf to the beaker of ethanol.
5. Place the beaker with ethanol inside the larger beaker of boiling water.
   - This will ensure that the ethanol (or isopropyl alcohol) does not get too hot.
6. Boil the leaf in the ethanol for 3 minutes to remove most of the chlorophyll.
   - The leaf should be almost white.
7. Carefully remove the leaf and put in Petri dish.
8. Cover the leaf with Lugol's iodine.
9. Wait two minutes and rinse leaf.
10. On the sketch of your leaf above, indicate which areas turned black and which did not.
11. Pour ethanol (or isopropyl alcohol) in organic waste container.

- What molecule is present where the leaf turned black?

Checkpoint B

BIOL 1406 – Photosynthesis Questions

Pre-Lab Questions

1. What type of energy is captured during photosynthesis?

   _____

2. Which is a final product of photosynthesis?
   a. Large amounts of ATP
   b. CO_2
   c. Sugars

3. Where in the cells does photosynthesis occur?
   a. Mitochondria
   b. Chloroplasts
   c. Nucleus

4. What technique will you use to separate pigments?

   _____

Post-Lab Questions

1. What are the reactants and products for the light reactions? What are the reactants and products for the Calvin cycle?

2. What would be the impact of a massive reduction in the amount of light energy reaching the Earth?

3. In which specific cells does photosynthesis occur and in which specific structures?

4. What is the purpose of the pigments in photosynthetic organisms and why would they differ between species?

5. What were your conclusions for the experiment using *Coleus* leaves?

6. If you had tested for glucose in the *Coleus* leaves you would have found that all parts test positive. How would you explain those results?

Goals

1. Identify the necessary components of the Results section.
2. Determine what type of information belongs in the Results section and what does not.
3. Determine how to make a complete data table.
4. Determine how to make a complete graph.

Activity 16.1: The Results Section

The Results section is where you present your data. This will be done in three ways: in text, in a data table, and in graph form. All three of these are required for your lab report Results section. The **data table** contains the numerical data that you collected in class. The **graph** takes some of those data and represents them visually for the reader. The text will point out trends in the data and direct the reader to the figures.

The text of the Results section is typically very straightforward. It is meant to highlight overall trends <u>without analysis</u>. This differs from the Discussion, which examines and analyzes the data while proposing ideas (it <u>discuss</u>es the experiment and results, if you will). The Results text should also direct the reader toward any data tables, graphs, or figures that are included in the report.

 Exercise 16.1: Results vs. Discussion

Examine the writing samples below. Which of the two should be in the Results section? Which should be in the Discussion?

A. More carbon dioxide was produced when glucose was used as a substrate (Table 1). Glucose metabolism produced 25% more carbon dioxide than fructose (Table 1). Sucrose produced the lowest carbon dioxide output as compared to the other sugars (Table 1). All trials showed a difference in carbon dioxide production when compared with the control (Graph 1).
B. All trials showed an increase in carbon dioxide production when compared with the control. As a result, I accept my hypothesis that the sugars would cause a change in carbon dioxide production. I predicted that glucose would result in the highest carbon dioxide output. This expectation was supported by the data. In addition, I predicted that sucrose metabolism would produce more carbon dioxide than fructose metabolism; this was not supported by the data.

Activity 16.2: Use of Figures

Figures are very important tools to help communicate your results to your reader. As mentioned previously, you will include two types of figures in your lab report: tables and graphs (your lab instructor will determine quantity and type). Note that tables and graphs are both different types of figures, but the terms 'table' and 'graph' should not be used interchangeably. The data table includes the numerical data; the graph is a pictorial representation of the data (or a <u>graph</u>ical representation, if you will).

Exercise 16.2: Table or Graph?

Is the figure below a table or a graph?

Plant Group	pH of Soil	Average Plant Growth (cm)
1	6.0	25.4
2	6.2	33.0
3	6.4	50.8
4	6.6	53.3
5	6.8	53.3
6	7.0	30.5
7	7.2	22.9

Is the figure below a table or a graph?

Trial	Block #1	Block #2	Block #3	Block #4
#1	15 cm	10 cm	60 cm	10 cm
#2	40 cm	13 cm	20 cm	10 cm
#3	10 cm	39 cm	184 cm	16 cm
Average	21.2 cm	20.2 cm	88 cm	12 cm

Is the figure below a table or a graph?

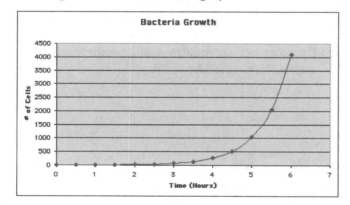

Is the figure below a table or a graph?

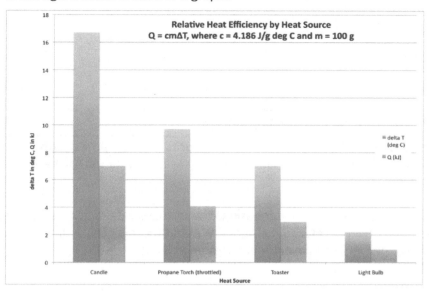

Is the figure below a table or a graph?

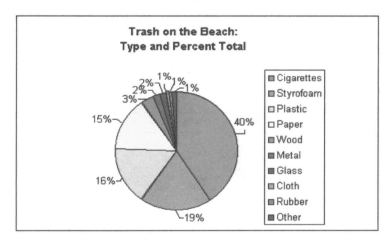

Is the figure below a table or a graph?

Mouse Number	Food	Week 1 Mass Gain	Week 2 Mass Gain	Total Mass Gained
1	Rice	6 g	8 g	14 g
2	Grain	5 g	4 g	9 g
3	Corn	8 g	4 g	12 g
4	Mixture	12 g	8 g	20 g

- Why is it important to use the proper terms when you refer to figures in your report?

Activity 16.3: Components of Figures

The figures in your report should stand alone. What does this mean? If your table or graph were on a page by itself (without the context of your lab report), could the reader discern what information the figure contains? If not, your figure is incomplete.

As such, your figures need labels to convey all necessary information. This includes a detailed title, column and row headers, data, and a number for which to refer to the figure. Without these pieces your figure may be confusing to the reader and/or fail to deliver the information you intend.

Exercise 16.3a: Recognizing Components of a Data Table
Examine the figure below. Identify the components of the figure.

Table 16.1. Soil moisture preference over time in *Pardosa mercularis*

	# of spiders (after 1 hr)	# of spiders (after 24 hrs)
0% soil moisture	2	0
1% soil moisture	3	1
5% soil moisture	2	1
10% soil moisture	3	8

o What type of figure is this?

o What is the title of the figure?

o What is the number of the figure?

o What data do the columns include?

o What data do the rows include?

o What information/overall trends can you deduce from this figure?

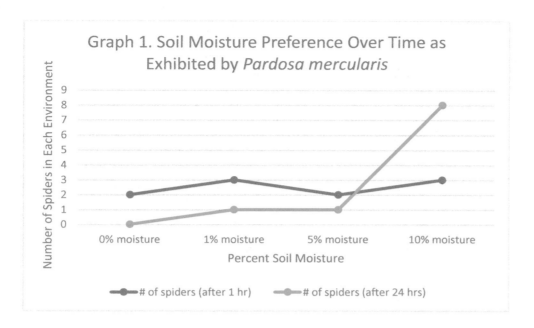

✋ **Exercise 16.3b: Recognizing Components of a Graph**

Examine the figure below. Identify the components of the figure.

o   What type of figure is this?

o   What is the title of the figure?

o   What is the number of the figure?

o   What does the x-axis indicate (i.e. what is its title)?

o   What does the y-axis indicate (i.e. what is its title)?

o   What is the difference between the two lines (i.e. what does the legend indicate)?

o   What information/overall trends can you deduce from this figure?

BIOL 1406 – Excel Workshop Questions

Pre-Lab Questions

1. In what section of your report should you include a table and a graph?

   _____

2. Which of the following does a complete data table need?
   a. Title
   b. Number
   c. Row/column headers
   d. Data
   e. All of the above

3. You should include an analysis of your data in the Results section.
   a. True
   b. False

4. Where do you accept your hypothesis in your report?
   a. Methods
   b. Results
   c. Discussion

Post-Lab Questions

1. What are the three necessary components of your Results section?

2. List and describe the necessary components of a data table.

3. List and describe the necessary components of a graph.

Goals

1. Identify the components of DNA nucleotides.
2. Explain the numbering of carbon atoms in the sugar components of nucleic acids.
3. Describe the method for extracting DNA from a sample.
4. Explain why all cells contain DNA.

Activity 17.1: DNA components

All life transfers information from one generation to the next in the form of deoxyribonucleic acid or **DNA**. Because of this, we call DNA the molecule of heredity. The DNA within cells contains information arranged in units called genes, which work to direct the development and maintenance of the organism.

The monomers that make up nucleic acids, including DNA, are **nucleotides** composed of three subunits: a phosphate group, a pentose sugar, and a nitrogenous base (Figure 17.1). The phosphate group is bound to the pentose sugar, which has five carbon atoms. In DNA, the pentose sugar is **deoxyribose**. Bound to the deoxyribose is a nitrogenous base. There are four different kinds of nucleotides found in DNA and each has a different nitrogenous base: adenine (A), thymine (T), cytosine (C), and guanine (G).

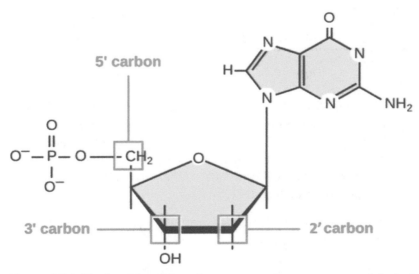

Figure 17.1. Nucleotide with carbon atoms of pentose sugar labeled

When nucleotides are connected by covalent **phosphodiester bonds**, they form a strand called a **polynucleotide**. Two strands of polynucleotides make up a molecule of DNA, which has a double helix shape like a ladder twisted into a spiral. The sides of the DNA ladder consist of the phosphate groups and the pentose sugars. Each rung of the DNA ladder is made of two nitrogenous bases, one base coming from each polynucleotide strand. As Figure 17.2 shows, the bases are held together by hydrogen bonds and each pair follows specific rules. Adenine only pairs with thymine and cytosine only pairs with guanine. Adenine (A) and thymine (T) can pair up because two hydrogen bonds connect them, while cytosine (C) and guanine (G) pair with three hydrogen bonds.

Deoxyribonucleic Acid (DNA)

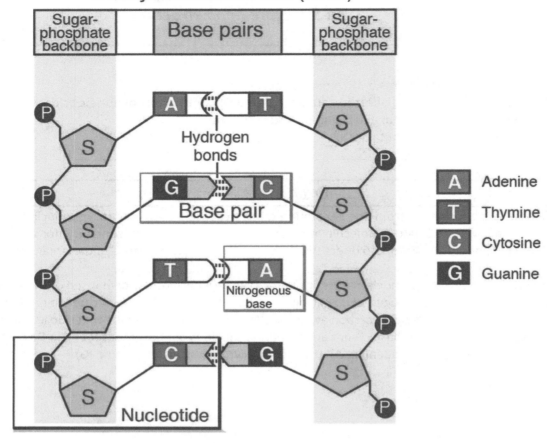

Figure 17.2 DNA molecule and components

The two strands of polynucleotides in DNA run antiparallel to one another, meaning they are in opposite directions. The direction a polynucleotide runs can be determined by the orientation of the pentose sugars located in each strand. As seen in Figure 17.1, when the carbon atoms in the sugar molecule are numbered, the fifth carbon (called the 5 prime [5'] carbon) is connected to the phosphate group. The examination of a molecule of DNA reveals that the 5' and 3' positions of one polynucleotide are upside down when compared to the other polynucleotide (Figure 17.3).

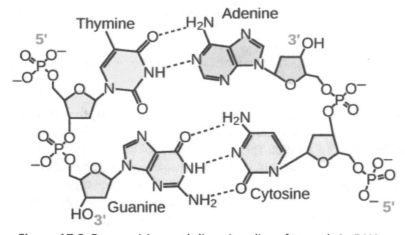

Figure 17.3. Base-pairing and directionality of strands in DNA

For the diagram of DNA below:

1. Draw a box around a nucleotide and label its components.
2. Fill in the nitrogenous bases on the second polynucleotide strand per the base-paring rules.
3. Draw the correct number of hydrogen bonds between the base pairs.
4. Label the ends of each polynucleotide strand with their primes (hint: 5' or 3' based on the orientation of the pentose sugar).

Activity 17.2: DNA Extraction

Each cell in an organism contains a package of genetic information in the form of DNA. In prokaryotes, most of the DNA is found in one circular chromosome in the nucleoid region, while eukaryotes have many linear chromosomes within the nucleus. Scientists refer to the entirety of the genetic information found in an organism as its **genome**.

If you want to extract DNA from an organism, a eukaryote is a good choice since eukaryotes have more and typically longer chromosomes compared to prokaryotes. For example, if the 46 chromosomes from one human cell were laid end to end, the DNA would measure almost 2 meters long. Taking your sample from a multicellular eukaryote would be an even better choice since your sample would likely contain thousands, perhaps millions, of cells. Extracting the DNA from many cells will result in clumps of DNA molecules that can be observed with your unaided eye. Plants are excellent candidates for extracting and observing DNA because they commonly possess multiple copies of DNA in the cells of their nuclei. Most organisms are diploid and have two sets of chromosomes (2n) in their genomes, but many plants have 4n, 6n, 8n, 10n, or even 12n! This phenomenon is termed **polyploidy** and the cultivated strawberry is octoploid with 8n.

Because the DNA in eukaryotic cells is protected inside the cell membrane and the nuclear envelope, both will need to be broken to extract the DNA. For plants or fungi, it is also necessary to break the cell walls around each cell. You will accomplish this with a combination of mechanical and chemical means, resulting in a solution of lysed cells. Crushing cells is one way to break the membranes. Another way is to use detergent, as it interacts with the phospholipids to disrupt the membrane structure. In order to fit all the DNA into the nucleus, eukaryotic chromosomes are packaged with proteins to form **chromatin**, so it is also beneficial to remove those proteins. Bromelain, a proteolytic enzyme that digests proteins, is found in pineapple. Pineapple juice can be added to the solution of lysed cells to help release the DNA. You will not be able to see the DNA initially because it is soluble in water. However, it is not soluble in alcohol. Adding an alcohol, such as ethanol or isopropyl alcohol, to the solution will cause the DNA will precipitate out of the solution. As the numerous molecules of DNA are not soluble in alcohol, they will clump together in a mass that can be easily seen.

 Exercise 17.2a: Samples for DNA Extraction

Your instructor will assign samples to your group for DNA extraction. Write hypotheses for whether or not you can extract DNA from the samples.

Hypothesis for Sample #1:

Hypothesis for Sample #2:

Checkpoint A

Exercise 17.2b: DNA Extraction

Materials needed: samples, small test tube, plastic funnel, sealable plastic bag, cheesecloth or filter paper 5-cm², 10 mL graduated cylinder, test tube rack, canned 100% pineapple juice, Cell Lysis Solution (detergent and salt), cold DNA Precipitation Solution (isopropyl alcohol)

1. Put your sample into a plastic bag and seal bag. With your fingers, squash the sample into a puree.
2. Using the graduated cylinder, measure 10 mL of Cell Lysis Solution. Pour into bag with strawberry and swish together for 1 minute.
   a. **Try to mix without creating bubbles**.
3. Add 1 mL of pineapple juice, reseal bag, and gently mix.
4. Place test tube in test tube rack and put funnel into the top of the test tube.
5. Line the funnel with a square of cheesecloth or filter paper.
6. SLOWLY pour a small amount of mixture into the funnel.
7. Let solution drip for 15 drops. DO NOT ALLOW ANY SOLIDS TO FALL INTO TEST TUBE. This solution is the lysate. Keep close track of how much lysate accumulates in the test tube.
8. Carefully remove and discard the cheesecloth and remnants of your sample.
9. Add alcohol (DNA Precipitation Solution) to the test tube until the tube is half full.
10. Observe for at least three minutes.
11. The DNA will slowly rise from the lysate layer up into the alcohol.
    a. Tiny bubbles will begin to form within the matrix of the DNA.
12. Eventually, the DNA will fully precipitate out of the lysate and float in the alcohol. Record your results for the sample in Table 17.1.
13. Wash plastic bag and funnel and perform the steps again for each sample assigned to your group.

Clean-up

➢ Pour the solution in the beaker (contains ethanol) into waste container, not down the sink.
➢ Wash all items and return to the kit.

Table 17.1. DNA Extraction Results

Sample	Was DNA Extracted?	Did the result support your hypothesis?

- Compare your results with those of other groups. What other samples contained DNA?

- Describe the appearance of the extracted DNA.

Checkpoint B

Pre-Lab Questions

1. DNA is a
    a. protein.
    b. carbohydrate.
    c. nucleic acid.

2. The monomers of DNA are

    _____.

3. In DNA, adenine bonds with
    a. guanine.
    b. cytosine.
    c. thymine.

4. The strawberry you will use in lab is an octoploid—it has _____ sets of chromosomes.

Post-Lab Questions

1. What different components are needed to synthesize (make) a molecule of DNA?

2. What are the pairing rules for DNA?

3. What was the purpose of mashing the strawberry and adding the Cell Lysis solution?

4. The primary ingredient of the DNA Precipitation solution is alcohol. What does it do?

5. Bruce successfully extracts DNA from an unknown sample. He has not yet analyzed the DNA, but Peter wants to know if the sample is from an animal or plant. Can Bruce give Peter a definite answer at this point? Why or why not?

6. Why would it have been more accurate to refer to the strawberry DNA we extracted as chromatin?

Goals

1. Explain how Meselson and Stahl's experiment confirmed the semiconservative model of DNA replication.
2. List the steps of DNA replication and describe the important molecules involved.
3. Model the process of DNA replication.

Activity 18.1: The Process of DNA Replication

The structure of the DNA molecule has several specific hallmarks. Individual nucleotides are covalently bound into polynucleotide strands by phosphodiester bonds. Each polynucleotide strand displays directionality; that is, each strand runs in the 5' to 3' direction with an unbound phosphate group at the 5' end and an unbound hydroxyl group at the 3' end. The two strands run antiparallel to one another (in opposite directions). The two strands are held together by hydrogen bonds between nitrogenous bases. The bases pair up according to Chargaff's rule: adenine and thymine are held together by two hydrogen bonds while cytosine and guanine are held together by three hydrogen bonds. These details mean that if the orientation and sequence of one strand is known, the orientation and sequence of the other strand can easily be determined.

DNA's unique structure also informs how DNA is replicated. Each polynucleotide strand provides a template for the other complementary polynucleotide strand. In 1958, molecular biologists Matthew Meselson and Franklin Stahl devised a series of experiments to determine how preexisting DNA molecules were used to replicate more copies. Their work supported the **semiconservative replication** model of DNA replication, in which each of the two new DNA molecules contain one old strand from the parent molecule and one new strand.

For semiconservative replication to occur, the double-stranded DNA must be separated into single polynucleotide strands. This allows each parent strand to act as a template on which new strands are built. Since hydrogen bonds between nitrogenous bases connect the two strands of DNA, these must be broken to separate the strands. The locations where the separation first occurs are called **origins of replication**. Prokaryotes have one circular chromosome and only one origin of replication, while eukaryotes may have hundreds or even a few thousand origins on their linear chromosomes (Figure 18.1).

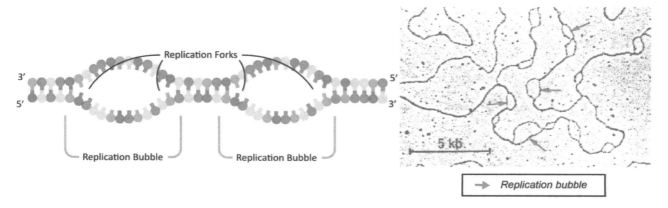

Figure 18.1. Origins of DNA replication.

The initiation of DNA replication occurs at these origins of replication, which have a specific sequence recognized by special proteins that bind to the DNA molecule. The binding of these proteins signals **helicase** to begin its job. Helicase breaks the hydrogen bonds between the base pairs and creates the replication bubble. At each end of the replication bubble is a Y-shaped region where the DNA helix is being unwound. This region is referred to as the **replication fork**. Once the helix is unwound, **single-strand binding proteins** (SSB or SSBP) bind to the single-stranded DNA and prevent the strands from reconnecting.

The unwinding of DNA may cause supercoiling in the double helix where the strands of DNA have not yet been separated by helicase. These supercoils are relaxed by **topoisomerase**. Topoisomerase binds to the DNA helix ahead of the replication fork (and helicase) and cuts the sugar-phosphate backbone to relieve the tension in the supercoil.

Synthesis of new DNA, however, is the whole purpose of replication. **DNA polymerases** use the parent DNA strands as templates. DNA polymerases ride on the parent stands, identifying which nucleotides to add to the new strand. However, DNA polymerases cannot start DNA synthesis independently. This is because DNA polymerases can only add nucleotides to the 3' hydroxyl group of an existing nucleotide with the creation of a phosphodiester bond. Luckily, **primase** will base-pair some RNA nucleotides to the parent DNA strand. This short segment is called a **primer** and is usually 9-12 nucleotides long. Once primers are paired to both parent strands, a DNA polymerase (**DNA polymerase III** in prokaryotes) adds DNA nucleotides to the 3' ends of the primers.

Since DNA polymerases can add new nucleotides only to the 3' end of an existing nucleotide, a new stand of DNA is synthesized in a 5' to 3' direction only. To initiate DNA replication, a primase adds a short complementary RNA primer, and a DNA polymerase adds DNA nucleotides to its 3' end.   As the two polynucleotide strands in DNA are antiparallel, synthesis of the new DNA strands must be accomplished in two different ways. One new strand will be synthesized continuously toward the replication fork. This is the **leading strand**. The other strand will be synthesized away from the replication fork in a series of small fragments, still in the 5' to 3' direction. These fragments are called **Okazaki fragments**, which are later joined to form a continuous chain of nucleotides. This strand is the **lagging strand**. Primase must add a primer to initiate synthesis of each Okazaki fragment. DNA polymerase extends the primers by base-pairing new DNA nucleotides and slides off the parent stand when the next Okazaki fragment is encountered. DNA polymerase then moves to a primer closer to the replication fork and continues base-pairing until all the necessary Okazaki fragments have been synthesized.

The RNA primers on the new strands must be replaced by DNA nucleotides. A DNA polymerase (**DNA polymerase I** in prokaryotes) removes the RNA nucleotides in the primer and replaces them with DNA nucleotides. At this point, the leading strand is complete. However, the lagging strand still contains gaps in the sugar-phosphate backbone between each Okazaki fragment. **Ligase** identifies and creates a phosphodiester bond between the 5' phosphate and 3' hydroxyl groups of the fragments to complete the lagging strand.

Exercise 18.1a: Complementary Strand

Examine the following DNA strand. Write in what the complementary strand should look like.

3' TACCAGTACGTTACGACGCCAGTCG 5'

Exercise 18.2a: Creating DNA nucleotide monomers

You will use two-dimensional pieces (shown in Figure 18.2) to represent the components of nucleic acids. Even though these are not three-dimensional models of the pieces of DNA, they should help you better understand DNA structure and DNA replication.

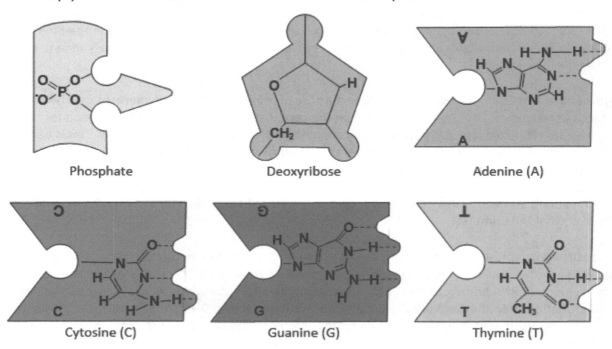

Figure 18.2. Representatives of DNA components

Materials needed: 16 deoxyribose pieces, 16 phosphate pieces, 4 adenine (A) pieces, 4 cytosine (C) pieces, 4 guanine (G) pieces, 4 thymine (T) pieces.

1. Gather your puzzle pieces. Identify which puzzle pieces correspond with each component of a nucleotide.
   - The pentose sugar is represented by _____
   - The phosphate is represented by _____
   - The nitrogenous bases are represented by _____

2. Notice the carbons in the pentose sugar are numbered from 1' (one prime) to 5' (five prime) as illustrated in Figure 18.3.
3. Using Figure 18.3 as a model, join together the correct puzzle piece components to form 16 **independent** nucleotides.
4. You **will not connect** the nucleotides together, as you need to wait until the next exercise.

5. Check with your instructor before moving on!

Checkpoint A

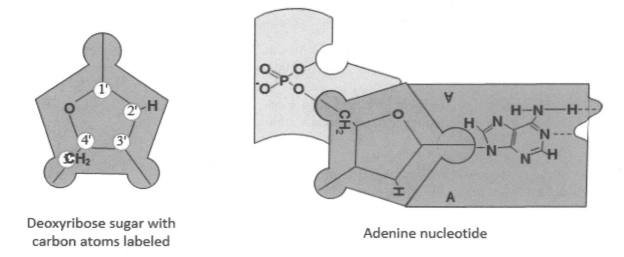

Deoxyribose sugar with
carbon atoms labeled

Adenine nucleotide

Figure 18.3. Deoxyribose structure and sample nucleotide

- To which carbon of deoxyribose is the nitrogenous base attached?

- To which carbon of deoxyribose is the phosphate group attached?

A DNA molecule consists of two **anti-parallel** strands, meaning that the strands run in opposite direction to each other. Each strand is a sequence of nucleotides that are held together by covalent **phosphodiester bonds**. The two strands, however, are held together by **hydrogen bonds** between bases. Each base only bonds to its complementary base (adenine with thymine, cytosine with guanine). In a cell, DNA is never created without a template, but we need to produce a new DNA molecule. TO MAXIMIZE YOUR UNDERSTANDING OF DNA SYNTHESIS, YOU SHOULD CREATE YOUR DNA STRAND SIMILAR TO HOW THE CELL PRODUCES IT. In a cell, the DNA nucleotides are slightly different than the ones you have created. In reality, before they are added to a DNA strand the nucleotides are actually triphosphates. Instead of having just one phosphate group on the 5' carbon, it is actually a triphosphate group. These triphosphates look very similar to the well-known ATP molecule (adenosine triphosphate). When a nucleotide is added to a DNA strand, the bond between the phosphate groups is broken. The breaking of this bond releases the energy needed to bond the phosphate of the incoming nucleotide to the 3' carbon of the deoxyribose sugar of the terminal nucleotide of the existing strand.

Exercise 18.2b: Create a DNA molecule

Materials needed: DNA nucleotides created in Exercise 18.2a

1. Using your nucleotides, build a four-nucleotide strand with this sequence: **5' TTGC 3'.**
   a. Check the strand. Do you and your lab partners agree that it's correct?

2. Now create the complementary strand of your existing DNA strand.
   a. What is the sequence of your complementary strand?

3. Write the sequences of your two DNA molecules below:
   Strand 1:

   Strand 2:

   *Check with your instructor before moving on!

Checkpoint B

Exercise 18.2c: Duplicate the DNA molecule

Materials needed: DNA nucleotides created in Exercise 18.2a; DNA molecule created in Exercise 18.2b

1. Now that you have created your starting (double-stranded) molecule of DNA, you will **begin the process of DNA replication <u>by separating the two puzzle strands from one another</u>**. Each of these strands will serve as the template for creating a new strand.

- What enzyme is responsible for separating the two DNA strands from one another?

- What types of bonds are being broken during the process of separating the two strands of DNA?

2. Although you will not simulate this with your puzzle pieces, what molecule holds the two strands of DNA apart from one another after they have been separated? And what enzyme will help relieve tension along the non-replicating parts of the DNA molecule?

3. Next, Primase creates primers for DNA polymerase to build the new strands of DNA. The RNA primer gives DNA polymerase III something to attach to, to begin creating new strands of DNA. This is another step you will not simulate with your puzzle pieces, though it is critical to the process of DNA replication.

4. DNA polymerase III adds DNA nucleotides starting where the primer leaves off, going in the 5'-3' direction. **<u>To each of the original strands of DNA</u> (from step 1), you will start adding DNA nucleotides (pretending the primer is present). Using your unlinked nucleotides, add the complementary nucleotide(s) one at a time <u>starting at the 5' end and adding new nucleotides only to the 3' end</u>.**

5. At the end of this process, you should have 2 identical DNA molecules, each made up of 2 strands of complementary DNA. Show your instructor your completed molecules.

Checkpoint C

BIOL 1406 – DNA Replication Questions

Pre-Lab Questions

1. DNA replication is
   a. conservative.
   b. semiconservative.
   c. dispersive.

2. In DNA, cytosine bonds with

   _____.

3. _____ adds DNA nucleotides during replication.
   a. DNA polymerase
   b. Helicase
   c. Ligase

4. During synthesis, the _____ strand contains Okazaki fragments.

Post-Lab Questions

1. Make a list of the enzymes that participate in DNA replication. What is the function of each enzyme?

2. Rick tells Morty he only needs to know the nucleotide sequence of one strand in a DNA molecule to know the sequence of the other strand. Why is Rick correct?

3. DNA polymerase creates phosphodiester bonds when synthesizing new DNA strands. Why is this necessary?

4. If all the ligase in a cell is mutated and inactive, how would this affect DNA replication?

5. At the end of Exercise 18.3c, you had two DNA molecules. Why should these molecules be identical to the DNA molecule you started with?

EL CENTRO CAMPUS BIOL 1406 PBL
Mitosis & Meiosis

Goals
1. Identify the phases of mitosis in animal and plant cells.
2. Model phases of mitosis in an animal cell.
3. Explain how haploid cells are created in meiosis.
4. Recognize homologous chromosome pairs and describe their characteristics.
5. Compare mitosis and meiosis.

Activity 19.1: The Cell Cycle

The cell theory states that new cells arise from the division of preexisting cells. In eukaryotic organisms cells are produced by two different types of cell division. The first type of cell division is **mitosis**, which results in the production of two daughter cells from a single parent cell. The daughter cells are genetically identical to the original parent cell. The second type of cell division is **meiosis**, which results in the production of cells that contain half the genetic material of the parent cell. Before mitosis or meiosis, the cell goes through a phase called **interphase** (see Figure 1). During this lengthy phase the cell undergoes its normal cellular functions and grows. At one point, called the **S phase**, the cell replicates its DNA in preparation for cell division.

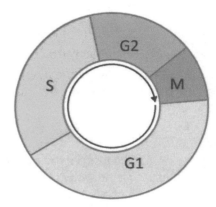

THE CELL CYCLE
➤ **Interphase (G_1, S, G_2):** 90% of Cell Cycle
➤ **M-phase (Mitosis or Meiosis):** 10 % of Cell Cycle

Figure 19.1. The Cell Cycle

Mitosis, one type of karyokinesis, refers to the division of the nuclear material and the process can be divided into different phases:

- **Prophase**
  - Chromosomes that were duplicated during interphase shorten and are now referred to as **sister chromatids**, which are attached at the centromere
  - Centrioles migrate to the poles of the cell (animal cells only)
  - Mitotic spindle forms from the poles of the cell toward the equator
  - Nuclear envelope starts to disintegrate

- **Late prophase**
  - Nuclear envelope completely disintegrates
  - Microtubules that form the spindle, also called mitotic fibers, begin binding to the sister chromatids
  - Prometaphase cannot be distinguished from prophase using the light microscope

- **Metaphase**
  - Sister chromatids, attached to mitotic fibers at the centromere, line up across the center, or metaphase plate, of the cell

- **Anaphase**
  - o Sister chromatids separate at the centromeres and are pulled to the poles of the cell by the mitotic spindle
- **Telophase**
  - o New daughter nuclei and nuclear envelopes form
  - o Chromosomes uncoil
  - o Mitotic spindle breaks down

The division of the cytoplasm, **cytokinesis**, occurs during or after telophase and produces two separate cells. For cell division to produce genetically identical daughter cells, both karyokinesis (mitosis) and cytokinesis must occur. Together, these two processes are the **mitotic phase**.

Animals and plant cells both undergo mitosis to generate new somatic cells. However, the stages of mitosis can appear different due to the presence (in plant cells) or absence (in animal cells) of the cell wall. In animal cells, cytokinesis starts with a cleavage furrow that eventually pinches in, dividing the cell in two. In plants, vesicles containing cell wall materials fuse to form a cell plate between the newly formed nuclei.

 Exercise 19.1a: Mitosis in Plants and Animals   *Lecture*
- Plant: Observe the micrograph of the onion root tip. Identify cells for each phase of mitosis. Which phase was the most difficult to find?

- Animal: Observe the micrograph of the whitefish blastula, a very young fish embryo that is rapidly dividing. Identify cells for each phase of mitosis.
  Which phase was the most difficult to find?

Activity 19.2: Modeling Mitosis

Within a multicellular organism there can be many different types of cells performing a variety of functions. Cells referred to as **somatic cells** can be skeletal muscle cells which aid in movement by their ability to contract or cone cells in the retina that allow colors to be seen. These cells are **diploid**, meaning that each type of chromosome comes in pairs. Each pair consists of a maternal chromosome originating from the egg of the organism's mother and a paternal chromosome originating from the sperm of the organism's father.

In the following activities you will use pipe cleaners to simulate chromosomes and plastic straws to represent the different genes found on those chromosomes in one of your somatic cells: an epithelial cell lining the stomach. These cells do not last long in the harsh environment of the stomach, and must be frequently replaced through mitotic division. As the cell is somatic it will have pairs of each chromosome type, consisting of a maternal and paternal chromosome. These are the same size to indicate they are the same type of chromosome and carry the same genes, as represented by the pieces of straw. If the genes on the maternal and paternal chromosome are the same form, they will be the same color. However, the genes they carry may be different forms or **alleles**. Different alleles for the same gene will be in the same location, but will be represented by different colors of straw.

Here is what your cell should look like in interphase:

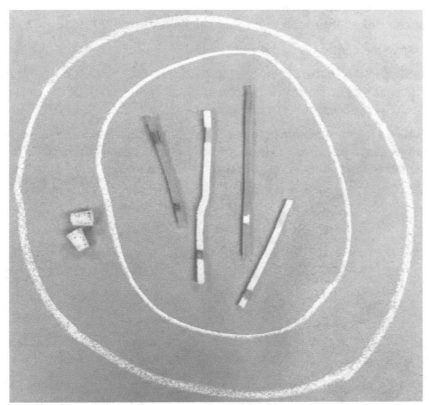

Figure 19.2. Simulated Diploid Cell in Interphase, 2n = 4

 Exercise 19.2a: Interphase and Mitotic Phase Simulation

Materials needed: 2 sets of 4 pipe cleaners (2 long and 2 short of each color) with straw "genes", 4 cork "centrioles," chalk

Maternal chromosome color: <u>ORANGE</u>   Paternal chromosome color: <u>WHITE</u>

1. **Create your cell:** Draw a large circle on your desk using a piece of chalk; this circle represents the nuclear envelope. Draw another circle even larger around the nuclear envelope; this circle represents the plasma membrane of the cell. Put two "centrioles" (represented by corks) near the nucleus. Throughout the exercise, you should fill in Figure 19.3.

2. **Add your chromosomes:** Your cell will have a total of four chromosomes. Add your pipe cleaner chromosomes so that your cell looks similar to the adjacent figure (be sure your straw "genes" are positioned appropriately). You will notice that you have two pairs that are similar. The maternal chromosomes are one color and the paternal chromosomes are the other color—we will discuss these in more detail in Activities 19.3 and 19.4. Your cell is now in **INTERPHASE – G1 PHASE**.

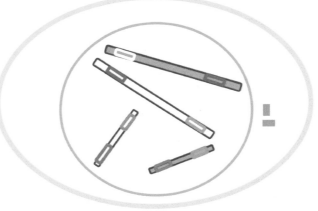

3. **INTERPHASE**: Replicate your chromosomes by adding copies of your chromosomes; twist the pipe cleaners together to represent where the sister chromatids would be joined at the centromeres. Also, replicate your centrioles. After replication your cell is now in **INTERPHASE – G2 PHASE.**

4. **PROPHASE**: Move the centrioles to the ends (poles) of the cell. Erase the nuclear membrane.

5. **LATE PROPHASE:** Use the chalk to draw lines to represent the spindle fibers. Draw 4 lines inside the cell, so that the lines extend from one pair of centrioles to the center of the cell and four lines extend from the opposite pair of centrioles to the center of the cell.

6. **METAPHASE:** Move the chromosomes to the center of the cell to simulate the chromosomes lining up on the metaphase plate. The order of the chromosome pairs does not matter. Your chromosomes and chalk-drawn spindle fibers should look similar to the figure below.

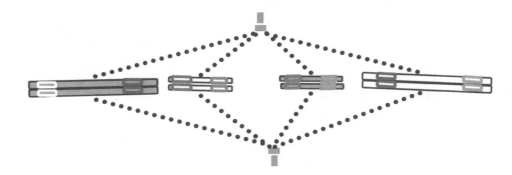

7. **ANAPHASE**: Loosen your chromosomes around the "centromere", and pull the sister chromatids apart; guide these now individual chromosomes to opposite poles, erasing the chalk spindle fibers as you go (this simulates the retracting of the microtubules to pull the chromosomes to each pole).

8. **TELOPHASE:** Draw a chalk "nuclear envelope" around each group of chromosomes, forming two nuclei.

9. **CYTOKINESIS:** Draw a chalk "plasma membrane" around each nucleus, forming two cells

- Compare the daughter cells. Do they contain identical or different chromosomes? Why?

Checkpoint A

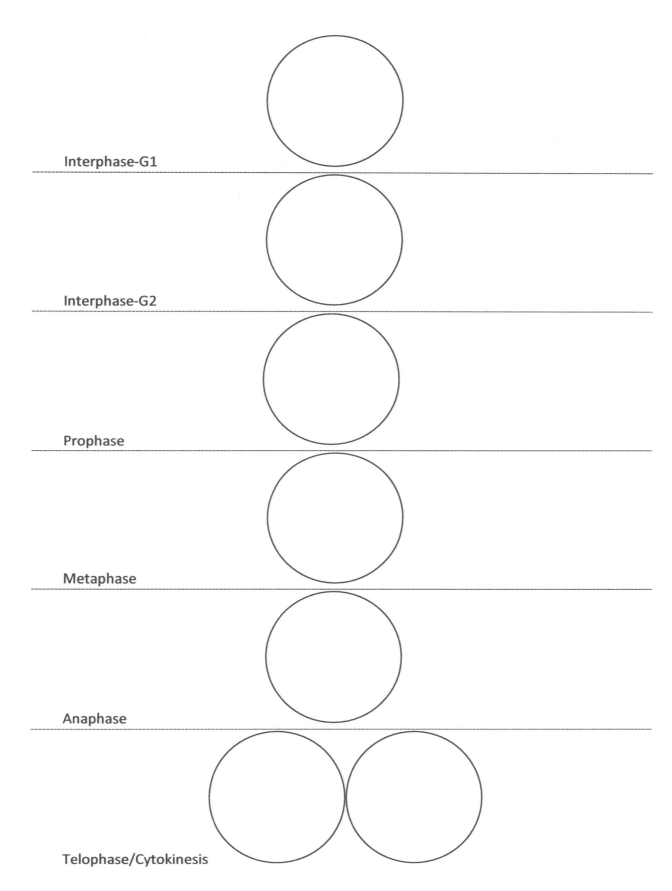

Interphase-G1

Interphase-G2

Prophase

Metaphase

Anaphase

Telophase/Cytokinesis

Figure 19.3. Phases in the Cell Cycle

Mitosis & Meiosis- 153

Activity 19.3: Meiosis

The production of gametes is required for sexual reproduction. Many eukaryotic organisms, both multicellular and unicellular, employ some form of meiosis to reproduce. **Meiosis** reduces the number of chromosomes so that the daughter cells contain half the amount of genetic material as compared to the parent cell. Many multicellular organisms, such as animals, are composed of two types of cells: somatic cells and gametes. Somatic cells, which include body cells other than sex cells, are **diploid** (2n) and contain two sets of chromosomes. Certain cells in the body, called **gametocytes** (or germ cells), undergo meiosis to produce haploid **gametes**. **Haploid** (n) cells contain just one set of chromosomes. In many organisms, the gametes are eggs and sperm. When gametes fuse at fertilization, a diploid **zygote** is formed. The zygote contains one set of chromosomes from each parent. For each maternal chromosome there is a corresponding paternal chromosome that is similar in appearance and gene composition. These pairs of corresponding chromosomes are called **homologous** pairs.

As in mitosis, DNA replication occurs during the S phase of interphase for meiosis. Following replication, each chromosome consists of two sister chromatids that are joined by a centromere. While meiosis possesses many similarities to mitosis, great differences also exist. Most noticeably, meiosis involves two successive divisions of the nucleus (karyokinesis I and karyokinesis II) and cytoplasm to produce four haploid cells.

Meiosis I
- **Prophase I**
  - Chromosomes condense, the nuclear envelope disappears and spindle forms
  - Homologous chromosomes synapse (pair up) to form **tetrads** consisting of four chromatids
  - Crossing over of chromosome segments between non-sister chromatids occurs
- **Late Prophase I**
  - Attachment of microtubules to tetrads; movement of tetrads toward metaphase plate
- **Metaphase I**
  - Tetrads line up along midplane of cell (metaphase I plate); homolog shuffling occurs.
- **Anaphase I**
  - Homologous pairs separate and are pulled to the poles of the cell by the spindle fibers
- **Telophase I**
  - New daughter nuclei and nuclear envelopes may reform; chromosomes may uncoil

Cytokinesis occurs during or after Telophase I.

Each new nucleus contains only one set of chromosomes and is haploid at this point in Meiosis

Meiosis II
- **Prophase II**
  - Chromosomes condense (if uncoiled), the nuclear envelope disappears and spindle forms
- **Late Prophase II**
  - Attachment of microtubules to chomatids; movement of chromosomes toward metaphase plate
- **Metaphase II**
  - Sister chromatids line up along metaphase II plate
- **Anaphase II**
  - Sister chromatids separate and are pulled to the poles of the cell by the spindle fibers
- **Telophase II**
  - New daughter nuclei and nuclear envelopes reform and chromosomes uncoil

Cytokinesis occurs during or after Telophase II to produce two haploid cells from each cell at the end of Meiosis I. After undergoing both stages of meiosis, a total of four haploid cells are formed from the original diploid parent cell.

✏ **Exercise 19.3a: Cell Division and Meiosis**   *Lecture*

Why are there two rounds of cell division in meiosis?

Activity 19.4: Modeling Meiosis

Sexual reproduction requires two parents contributing gametes formed by meiosis. As you learned from the last activity, gametes are haploid and contain only one set of chromosomes. Except for their gametes, most sexually reproducing organisms are composed of diploid cells. The diploid cells contain two sets of chromosomes—a paternal set inherited from the father and a maternal set inherited from the mother. If we examine one chromosome for the maternal set, we can find a chromosome in the paternal set that is similar in shape, size, centromere location, and gene sequence. These chromosome "pairs" are called **homologous** chromosomes.

During Prophase I, the homologous chromosomes synapse to form tetrads. The tetrads separate during Anaphase I, resulting in the formation of two cells at the end of Meiosis I, each containing only one duplicated chromosome from each of the homologous pairs. As tetrads align randomly during Metaphase I, each daughter cell contains an assortment of paternal and maternal chromosomes.

For example, humans have a diploid number of 46 (2n=46), so you have 46 chromosomes in each of your cells. If we examine the DNA of your diploid cells, we see that 23 of the chromosomes were contributed by your mother (maternal) and 23 were contributed by your father (paternal). When you produce gametes (via meiosis), the homologous chromosomes (which were already duplicated in interphase and consist of sister chromatids) pair up to form 23 tetrads. The 23 tetrads align along the midplane of the cell during Metaphase I. If we look closely at the tetrads, the paternal chromosome might be on the left and the maternal on the right, or vice versa—it is random each time meiosis occurs. When the tetrads separate in Anaphase I, all the chromosomes on the right side will move to one pole of the cell, while all the chromosomes on the left will move to the other pole of the cell. This means the two cells at the end of Meiosis I are haploid (n=23), because they only contain one chromosome from each homologous pair. Since those chromosomes are still in the duplicated form, Meiosis II will separate the sister chromatids; thus, there will be four cells at the end of meiosis. This second division does not reduce the number of chromosome sets; it only separates the sister chromatids.

Something interesting occurs in many organisms when homologous chromosomes synapse in early Prophase I. Once tetrads have formed **crossing over** may occur, meaning sections of DNA between one maternal chromatid and one paternal chromatid (termed non-sister chromatids) can be exchanged. As a result, each of the four chromatids in a homologous pair will be different. Two will be purely maternal or paternal, while two will be **recombinant chromosomes** and contain sections of DNA they obtained during crossing over.

This may lead you to ask, "Why are recombinant chromosomes different?" Although a pair of homologous chromosomes has the same gene sequence, the genes themselves might be a different form. Different forms of a gene are called **alleles**. For example, there are different alleles for the gene that determines pigments in the iris of the eye, which results in different eye colors. While the iris pigment gene would be found on the same chromosome and in the same locus on the maternal and paternal chromosomes, the gene could be the allele for light eyes or the allele for dark eyes.

You examined mitosis in one of your somatic cells in Activity 19.2a. You will now examine meiosis to produce your gametes. In the following activities you will use the same pipe cleaners representing pairs of homologous chromosomes. The cells that produce gametes are gametocytes, which are diploid cells. These cells undergo interphase prior to meiosis just like somatic cells undergo interphase prior to mitosis.

 Exercise 19.4a: Crossing Over

Materials needed: 2 sets of 4 pipe cleaners (2 long and 2 short of each color) with straw "genes", 4 cork "centrioles," chalk

1. Restore your cell to G_1 as it looked at the end of step 2 in Exercise 19.2a. Examine your cell and its chromosomes to determine which colors of straw/paint represent which alleles as given in the following scenarios.

    *   Longer chromosomes: Assume the pink straw on the <u>long</u> **maternal chromosome** is the allele that codes for dark eyes and the white paint is the allele that codes for normal hemoglobin, the protein on red blood cells that carries oxygen. Assume the orange straw on the <u>long</u> **paternal chromosome** is the allele that codes for light eyes and the red paint is the allele that codes for sickle-cell hemoglobin, a mutated form of the hemoglobin protein. Table 19.1 summarizes this information.

	Chromosome color	Eye color allele	Hemoglobin allele
Long maternal chromosome	Orange	Pink straw (Dark eyes)	White paint (Normal hemoglobin)
Long paternal chromosome	White	Orange straw (Light eyes)	Red paint (Sickle hemoglobin)

Table 19.1. Chromosome and allele colors for the long pair of homologous chromosomes

    *   Shorter chromosomes: Assume the purple straw on the <u>short</u> **maternal chromosome** is the allele that codes for straight hair and the blue paint is the allele that codes for freckles. Assume the yellow straw on the <u>short</u> **paternal chromosome** is the allele that codes for curly hair and the green paint is the allele that codes for no freckles. Table 19.2 summarizes this information

	Chromosome color	Hair texture allele	Freckle allele
Short maternal chromosome	Orange	Purple straw (Straight hair)	Blue paint (Freckles)
Short paternal chromosome	White	Yellow straw (Curly hair)	Green paint (No freckles)

Table 19.2. Chromosome and allele colors for the short pair of homologous chromosomes

2. Label *Figure 19.3* so that it depicts which allele is which. Draw arrows from the labels to the alleles so that each chromosome is clearly defined.

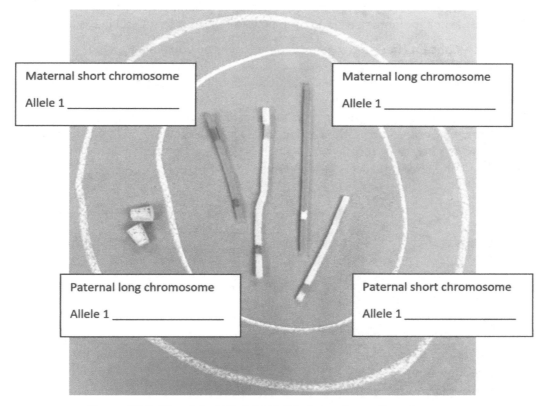

Maternal short chromosome

Allele 1 _____

Maternal long chromosome

Allele 1 _____

Paternal long chromosome

Allele 1 _____

Paternal short chromosome

Allele 1 _____

Figure 19.3. Simulated Diploid Cell in Interphase, 2n = 4

3. Now take your cell through S phase (as you did in Exercise 19.2a); your cell should now be in G2. This cell should look identical to your cell at the end of step 3 in Exercise 19.2a.

4. **Meiosis I, Prophase 1**: Bring the duplicated homologous chromosomes together so they "synapse" to form a tetrad.

Checkpoint B

5. Simulate crossing over by exchanging genes between the two chromosomes that are next to each other (i.e. adjacent non-sister chromatids); represent this by exchanging the straw 'genes' only on one end of the non-sister chromatids.

6. Now take your cell through the remaining steps of Meiosis I. Line up the tetrads on the **Metaphase I** plate, separate the homologous chromosomes to simulate **Anaphase I**, and draw the new nuclear envelopes around the newly-formed nuclei in **Telophase I**. Draw a new plasma membrane around each cell to represent Cytokinesis I.

    a. Concept check: How many daughter cells do you have? _____

    b. Are these daughter cells haploid or diploid? _____

7. Each of the cells you produced at the end of Meiosis I now needs to go through **Meiosis II**. One at a time simulate each cell as it goes through **Prophase II, Metaphase II, Anaphase II**, and **Telophase II** (don't forget to draw the new nuclear envelopes around the newly-formed nuclei). Be sure to draw a new plasma membrane around each new cell to represent Cytokinesis II.

    a. Concept check: How many daughter cells do you have? _____

    b. Are these daughter cells genetically identical to each other? _____

- Now examine your four daughter cells. *Each should contain a distinctly different set of chromosomes due to crossing over.* Compare the chromosomes in your daughter cells with the chromosomes you had prior to meiosis occurring (use Table 19.1 and Table 19.2). Fill out Table 19.3 to reflect the four different combinations of alleles in each of your daughter cells.

Table 19.3: Crossing Over		Gametes			
		Daughter Cell 1	Daughter Cell 2	Daughter Cell 3	Daughter Cell 4
Long Chromosome	Eye Color Gene (dark or light)				
	Hemoglobin Gene (normal or mutated)				
Short Chromosome	Hair Texture Gene (straight or curly)				
	Freckle Gene (freckles or no freckles)				
Are recombinant chromosomes present in cell?					

- Which cells contain recombinant chromosomes and what are the new combinations of traits?

Checkpoint C

BIOL 1406 – *Mitosis & Meiosis Questions*

Pre-Lab Questions

1. Mitosis is a type of cell division to produce
   a. Somatic cells
   b. Gametes
   c. Protein

2. Mitosis produces daughter cells that are identical to the parent cell.
   a. True
   b. False

3. Meiosis produces gametes that only contain half the amount of chromosomes and are therefore called _____.

4. The last phase of mitosis is cytokinesis.
   a. True
   b. False

Post-Lab Questions

1. What is the purpose of mitosis?

2. You focused on cell division in animals cells. How would the mitotic phase be different in plants?

3. What are the three main differences between mitosis and meiosis?

4. If a cell with a diploid number of 6 chromosomes (2n=6) undergoes meiosis, what will the cell look like after Telophase 1? Draw the result below:

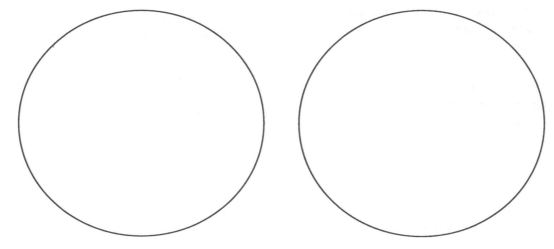

5. Chromosome 1 is one of the 23 pairs of chromosomes in humans. It is the largest human chromosome and spans about 249 million nucleotide base pairs, comprising over 4,300 genes. How many copies of chromosome 1 can we find in *your* somatic (non-sex) cells? Why are these copies called homologous? And how many copies will we find in your gametes (sex) cells?

6. What would happen if a tetrad does not separate during Anaphase I? Could the cell still produce any normal gametes?

Goals
1. Identify the necessary components of the Discussion section.
2. Determine what type of information belongs in the Discussion section and what does not.
3. Perform a literature search to find other studies to compare your work to.

Activity 20.1: The Discussion Section

The Discussion section is where you accept or reject your hypotheses (based upon the evidence you collected in class), discuss any mistakes/problems with the lab, suggest ways in which the lab could be improved, and compare your work with that of other scientists. If that sounds like a lot, it is! The Discussion section is typically the longest section of the report.

Your original hypotheses and predictions should be addressed in the first paragraph of your Discussion section. If the evidence you collected (i.e. the data included in the Results section) support your hypothesis, then you accept your hypothesis. If the evidence does not support your hypothesis, then you reject your hypothesis. As you write your Discussion section keep in mind that one experiment does not prove anything. You have simply collected data which will help to validate or invalidate the hypotheses you made.

 Exercise 20.1: Addressing the Hypotheses

Examine the writing samples below. Which of these would be appropriate for your lab report Discussion section?

A. I got the results as shown above. Since the carbon dioxide raised in the experiment my hypothesis was right. My hypothesis was proven. Anyone can see that carbon dioxide will go up as food is eaten. My prediction was correct.

B. All trials showed an increase in carbon dioxide production when compared with the control. As a result, I accept my hypothesis that the sugars would cause a change in carbon dioxide production. I predicted that glucose would result in the highest carbon dioxide output. This expectation was supported by the data. In addition I predicted that sucrose metabolism would produce more carbon dioxide than fructose metabolism; this was not supported by the data.

- What are some of the problems with the less-appropriate sample?

Activity 20.2: What Went Wrong?

When we perform experiments, we endeavor to be precise and accurate; however, even the best researchers make mistakes sometimes. This is to be expected, and is perfectly okay...as long as we admit to it! The Discussion section is where we explain to the reader what went wrong.

There are times during experiments when we know we've made mistakes. Maybe you realized halfway through your data collection that you were not following the proper methods. Maybe you observed mistakes being made by other groups. Either way, this is the time to discuss the mistakes.

 Exercise 20.2a: Mistakes Were Made...and We Know What They Were

Examine the writing samples below. Which of these would be appropriate for your lab report Discussion section?

A. During the experiment I observed two mistakes that may have affected the data. In Trial 3, two of the beetle larvae placed in the test tube were dead. This was not noted until after the trial was completed and lab clean-up had begun. This equates to the test tube for Trial 3 containing only eight living specimens instead of the 10 specimens that should have been present. In addition, the timer was accidentally turned off during Trial 7. This trial ran longer than the other trials, which were all accurately timed to one minute. These two mistakes may have contributed to the unexpected results I observed.

B. I noticed several mistakes being made during the lab. First, one group put two dead animals into their containers, and they didn't figure that out until lab was over. Then another group turned their timer off during their trial and didn't notice for like three minutes. This definitely affected the results because we got weird results and it was their fault.

- What are some of the problems with the less-appropriate sample?

There are other times during experiments when we do not know what mistakes have been made. We believe, to the best of our ability, that all methods were followed appropriately and correctly. And yet...the results do not support our original hypotheses. Inevitably we ask ourselves why the data did not turn out as predicted.

The Discussion section is the one place in your lab report (other than your original hypotheses and predictions) where you can include your opinion. If you have unexpected results, you will need to develop plausible explanations for why they might have occurred.

Exercise 20.2b: What Happened??

Examine the writing samples below. Which of these would be appropriate for your lab report Discussion section?

A. As is noted in Table 1, two of the trials resulted in unexpected results. The larvae in these two groups experienced higher respiratory rates than the other eight groups. This could have been due to low levels of the chemical being present. If the reagent was diluted the animals may not have experienced such high levels of respiratory suppression. Alternatively, if the reagent bottle was mislabeled, the chemical could have been a stimulant instead of the intended depressant.

B. If you look at Table 1 you'll see that not all of the data went correctly. There are two times in which the results were wrong. In Trial 8 it may have been because that group usually makes mistakes. I didn't see any this time, but they don't usually know what's going on and are always asking my group what they should be doing. So I don't know that they knew what they were supposed to do. Also in Trial 10 the larvae were really small and maybe they were scared and that is what caused them to respire more.

- What are some of the problems with the less-appropriate sample?

Activity 20.3: Literature Review

Many undergraduates are unfamiliar with what is necessary in conducting a **literature review** for a scientific and technical paper. The 'literature' here is not the type of literature you would read in an English class. Rather, literature in this context refers mainly to the primary literature; this is literature that has been published detailing other experiments performed by other scientists. It is referred to as being 'primary' because the people who write the reports are the same people who performed the experiments (much like you writing up your lab report!).

Primary sources are not the only appropriate sources for your report. Textbooks and other books, your class handouts, encyclopedias, and a few websites can also be used provided the authors are credible.

Performing a literature review can be tricky at first. It is not quite as simple as doing a quick internet search. Unfortunately much of what is online is not considered valid for an academic report. This is why you have been directed to avoid .com and .org sources, and to use .gov and .edu sources with caution. It is usually best to verify with your lab instructor if a certain website can be used in your report.

Where can you go to find valid sources for your report? The Library, of course! You can access library databases through the library website (https://www.dallascollege.edu/libraries/pages/default.aspx) or you can go directly to the library and ask the librarians for assistance (they would love to help you – go see them!).

You use your sources in the Discussion section just as you would any other source in any other location: to back up a point that you are making. Sometimes students get confused when using primary literature and think they have to summarize other research within their lab report. This is unnecessary and takes away from the report. Remember: your experiment is the star of your lab report!

Exercise 20.3: How to Use Sources in the Discussion Section

Examine the writing samples below. Which of these would be appropriate for your lab report Discussion section?

    A.   Another study was done that was similar to this one. The researchers at the University of Wisconsin found that nicotine in small doses could cause an increase in respiration. This is like what I did because the beetles I used respired less when a stimulant was used.

    B.   The results of this study reflect what has been found in previous research regarding respiration in beetles (Lennon, 2012).

- What are some of the problems with the less-appropriate sample?

Activity 20.4: Suggestions?

The last part of your Discussion section includes your thoughts on what you would change in the future if you were to conduct the experiment again. Maybe you would like to use a different organism. Maybe you would change how much time was used to conduct the experiment. Maybe you came up with ideas during the experiment that could be incorporated in the future – who knows?? Think back over the experiment and consider what you could differently to improve the outcomes.

 Exercise 20.4: What Would You Do Differently?

Examine the writing samples below. Which of these would be appropriate for your lab report Discussion section?

    A.   If I did this again I wouldn't use beetles. I would use something prettier like butterflies or something. Butterflies may also respond to nicotine.

    B.   Future experiments could increase the timed portion from one minute to five minutes. This experiment utilized a one minute timed period which was then multiplied by five to approximate a five-minute interval. Timing the experiment for a full five minutes could result in greater clarity regarding the data.

What are some of the problems with the less-appropriate sample?

BIOL 1406 – Analysis Workshop Questions

Pre-Lab Questions

1. In what section of your report should you accept/reject your hypothesis?
    _____

2. Which of the following would be an appropriate reference for a lab report?
    a. Wikipedia
    b. ILoveScience.com
    c. https://www.pinterest.com/biology
    d. Your textbook

3. Where do you discuss the step-by-step procedure you used to perform your experiment?
    a. Methods
    b. Results
    c. Discussion

Post-Lab Questions

1. What should the first paragraph of your Discussion section include?

2. What are some of the features of a quality literature review?

3. What elements should be included in your Discussion section?

 **EL CENTRO CAMPUS BIOL 1406 PBL**
Heredity – Direwolf Edition

Goals
1. Explain how alleles relate to genes.
2. Describe the difference between genotypes and phenotypes.
3. Distinguish between dominant and recessive alleles.
4. Distinguish between an organism's phenotype and genotype
5. Determine possible gametes from a given genotype.
6. Predict an offspring's phenotype and genotype.
7. Use a Punnett square to determine offspring genotype and phenotype probabilities for single-character crosses.

Activity 21.1: Genes and Alleles

A **gene** is a DNA sequence at a specific location on a chromosome that determines a particular characteristic. Humans have approximately 25,000 genes on 23 chromosome pairs. Genes are also the units of heredity for living organisms and for every characteristic (such as skin color, eye color, hair texture) there are different forms or varieties of the characteristic you could possess. These varieties are called **alleles**. For example, you have genes for eye color that you inherited from your parents. Because that gene is on two of your chromosomes—one you inherited from your mother and the other you inherited from your father—you have two copies (alleles) for that gene. The alleles for eye-color might code for light eyes or dark eyes.

A **genotype** is the set of alleles an organism has. Instead of writing out light eye allele and dark eye allele, we abbreviate the names of alleles. For our example we will designate the dark eye allele as **B** and the light eye allele as **b**. For eye color, you could have one of the following genotypes:

- **BB** – two dark eye alleles
- **Bb** – one dark eye allele, one light eye allele
- **bb** – two light eye alleles

A genotype of **Bb** would be considered **heterozygous**, as the two alleles are different from one another. An organism is said to be **homozygous** for a certain characteristic if it carries two of the same alleles, either **BB** or **bb** for our example.

Some alleles are dominant over other alleles. This means that the dominant allele masks the recessive allele. For our example, if you have one dark eye allele, you will have dark eyes no matter what the other allele is. Thus, if a person is **Bb**, she/he will have dark eyes, not a mixture of dark and light. Only if a person has two light eye alleles (**bb**) will the eyes be light. **B** is called the dominant allele and **b** is the recessive allele. This type of dominance is known as **complete dominance**. An individual is homozygous dominant if it carries two dominant alleles and homozygous recessive if it carries two recessive alleles.

A **phenotype** is the expression of a genotype. If you are heterozygous, the dominant allele will express itself over the recessive allele resulting in a phenotype for dark eyes. The recessive phenotype is only observed if two recessive alleles are present.

✏️ **Exercise 21.1: Considering Genotypes and Phenotypes, Complete Dominance** *Lecture*

If you are **BB**, your eyes will be _____.

If you are **Bb**, your eyes will be _____.

If you are **bb**, your eyes will be _____.

- Concept check: How many different phenotypes are produced by these three different genotypes?

Activity 21.2: Degrees of Dominance

Every gene has two alleles or forms. For many genes there is one dominant allele and one recessive allele; this is complete dominance as discussed above. Humans have many traits that follow the dominant-recessive system but many genes also interact with the environment to produce a certain phenotype. That is how some individuals can have eyes of two different colors.

Complete dominance is not the only way that two different alleles may interact to produce a phenotype. **Incomplete dominance** is a system in which two different alleles both contribute to the overall phenotype, but neither is completely expressed. For example we can examine hair texture. The **T** allele codes for curly hair while the **t** allele codes for straight hair. A person with curly hair is homozygous for the **T** allele, a person with straight hair is homozygous for the **t** allele. However, a person who is heterozygous at this locus will have wavy hair.

✏️ **Exercise 21.2a: Considering Genotypes and Phenotypes, Incomplete Dominance** *Lecture*

If you are "**TT**", your hair will be _____.

If you are "**Tt**", your hair will be _____.

If you are "**tt**", your hair will be _____.

- Concept check: How many different phenotypes are produced by these three different genotypes?

Another system of dominance is **co-dominance**. In this system, two different alleles fully contribute to the overall phenotype. Neither allele is fully or partially masked in this system. An example of this is displayed by sickle-cell anemia, a condition produced by a mutation in the hemoglobin protein. Hemoglobin is found in red blood cells and is responsible for carrying oxygen to the cells of your body. Normal hemoglobin (also called hemoglobin A) is coded for by the H^A allele. Mutated sickle hemoglobin (also called hemoglobin S) is coded for by the H^S allele. As these are alleles of the same gene, they are represented by the same letter, **H**. However, neither are written in lowercase, as they are both always expressed. The superscript (A or S) allows us to differentiate between the normal hemoglobin allele and the sickle hemoglobin allele. Individuals who are homozygous for the H^A allele produce only normal hemoglobin, and all of their red blood cells will be normal. Individuals who are homozygous for the **H^S** allele produce only sickle hemoglobin, and their red blood cells will be sickle-shaped. This results in Sickle Cell Disease (SCD), also known as sickle-cell anemia, which is characterized by lower concentrations of both oxygen and red blood cells in the blood. Individuals who are heterozygous produce both hemoglobin A and hemoglobin S, and their red blood cells are a combination of normal and sickle-shaped. People who are heterozygous at this locus are said to have Sickle Cell Trait (SCT); they typically do not display symptoms of sickle cell anemia, but have one copy of the mutated hemoglobin S allele that they can pass on to their children.

Exercise 21.2b: Considering Genotypes and Phenotypes, Co-Dominance *Lecture*

If you are **H^{A}H^A**, your red blood cells will be _____.

If you are **H^{A}H^S**, your red blood cells will be _____.

If you are **H^{S}H^S**, your red blood cells will be _____.

- Concept check: How many different phenotypes are produced by these three different genotypes?

Exercise 21.2c: What is the Phenotype?
Examine the following scenarios and determine what phenotypes will be produced by the given genotypes.

- Sansa has the following genotypes: **bb**, **Tt**, and **H^{A}H^A**. What phenotypes does Sansa display?

- Arya has the following genotypes: **Bb**, **tt**, and **H^{A}H^S**. What phenotypes does Arya display?

Exercise 21.2d: What is the Genotype?
Examine the following scenarios and determine what genotypes produced the given phenotypes.

- Jaime has light eyes, wavy hair, and has SCT. What possible genotypes does Jaime have?

- Robert has dark eyes, curly hair, and normal red blood cells. What possible genotypes does Robert have?

Activity 21.3: Producing Gametes

Almost all animals, including humans, are diploid but produce haploid **gametes** via meiosis. The haploid sperm carries one half of the father's alleles, and the haploid egg contains half of the mother's alleles. Upon fertilization the two haploid gametes produce a diploid zygote.

It is important to note that while humans are diploid organisms (with two alleles for each locus), their gametes are haploid (with only one allele for each locus). Let's look at an example using Sansa from Exercise 21.2c. Sansa has light eyes with a diploid genotype of **bb**. This means all of her somatic (body) cells contain two copies of the **b** allele. These alleles separate during meiosis to form the haploid gametes, each with one copy of the **b** allele. Sansa's alleles for hair texture and hemoglobin will also separate during meiosis with one copy of each allele ending up on each gamete. This is displayed in Table 21.1.

Table 21.1. Genotypes of Sansa's diploid somatic cells and haploid gametes

Sansa's diploid genotype	Sansa's haploid gamete 1	Sansa's haploid gamete 2
Eye color: **bb**	b	b
Hair texture: **Tt**	T	t
Hemoglobin: $H^A H^A$	H^A	H^A
Sum of alleles on each gamete	bTH^A	btH^A

Now using Arya, Jaime, and Robert from Exercises 21.2c and 21.2d, fill out Tables 21.2, 21.3, and 21.4.

Exercise 21.3a: Making haploid gametes from diploid somatic cells

Table 21.2. Genotypes of Arya's diploid somatic cells and haploid gametes

Arya's diploid genotype	Arya's haploid gamete 1	Arya's haploid gamete 2
Eye color:		
Hair texture:		
Hemoglobin:		
Sum of alleles on each gamete		

Table 21.3. Genotypes of Jaime's diploid somatic cells and haploid gametes

Jaime's diploid genotype	Jaime's haploid gamete 1	Jaime's haploid gamete 2
Eye color:		
Hair texture:		
Hemoglobin:		
Sum of alleles on each gamete		

Table 21.4. Genotypes of Robert 's diploid somatic cells and haploid gametes

Robert's diploid genotype	Robert's haploid gamete 1	Robert's haploid gamete 2
Eye color:		
Hair texture:		
Hemoglobin:		
Sum of alleles on each gamete		

Activity 21.4: Single Character Analysis

Now you will examine how a given characteristic can be passed down from parents to offspring. In a single-character analysis, a geneticist (or you!) can determine the likelihood that a certain trait will be passed on to offspring. To do this we utilize the genotypes of the parents and their gametes to examine what the potential genotypes of the offspring will be.

Let's look at an example using Catelyn and Ned. Catelyn has light eyes while Ned has dark eyes. They have five children: Sansa and Arya (as discussed above) and three boys. Robb has light eyes while Bran and Rickon have dark eyes.

- Sansa and Robb both have light eyes, like their mother. What is their genotype? _____
  (Hint: this should be easy as only one genotype codes for the light-eyed phenotype.)

- Arya, Bran, and Rickon all have dark eyes, like their father. What is their genotype? _____

Ah, determining the genotype for dark eyes isn't as straightforward, is it? Two different genotypes, **BB** and **Bb**, code for dark eyes. So which one do the three dark-eyed children have? Well let's take a closer look.

Catelyn has light eyes so her genotype is bb. So when her alleles separate into her gametes half of the gametes will contain **b** and the other half will contain **b** (surprise, surprise: all of her gametes contain **b**). She only has recessive **b** alleles to give to her gametes and her children. This means all of her children will inherit a recessive **b** from their mother. So that means that all of Catelyn's dark-eyed children must be heterozygous, **Bb**. Go ahead and write-in their genotype above if you haven't already.

Now we need to determine what Ned's genotype is. You might already have figured this out, but let's work it out anyway. We know that Ned has dark eyes, so he must be either **BB** or **Bb**. How can we determine which he is? By looking at his offspring, of course! Two of Ned's offspring, Sansa and Robb, have light eyes (**bb**). We already know that Sansa and Robb inherited a **b** from their mother Catelyn. But they each also had to inherit a **b** from their father Ned. That's the only way that Sansa and Robb could each have two **b** alleles and thus be homozygous recessive (**bb**) and have light eyes. So that means that Ned must be heterozygous, **Bb**. Ned has one **B** allele to give him dark eyes, but he also carries a **b** allele that can be inherited by his offspring. Table 21.5 summarizes the family's genetics.

Table21. 5. Genotypes and Phenotypes of Ned and Catelyn's Family

Individual	Phenotype	Genotype
Ned	Dark eyes	**Bb**
Catelyn	Light eyes	**bb**
Robb	Light eyes	**bb**
Sansa	Light eyes	**bb**
Arya	Dark eyes	**Bb**
Bran	Dark eyes	**Bb**
Rickon	Dark eyes	**Bb**

Once we know the genotypes of the two parents involved in a given analysis, we can determine the possible genotypes of their offspring using a Punnett Square. A Punnett Square is a handy device geneticists (or you!) can use to examine the potential outcomes of various genetic crosses.

We will use Catelyn and Ned once again for this analysis. We know that Catelyn's genotype is **bb** and that her gametes will all contain one recessive **b**. Ned's genotype is **Bb**; thus, half of his gametes will carry the dominant **B** while the other half will carry the recessive **b**. Table 21.6 shows the Punnett Square for the possible combinations of their gametes. Each of Ned's gametes is placed at the tops of the columns, and each of Catelyn's gametes is placed at the fronts of the rows. The possible combinations of their gametes represent the possible genotypes their offspring could have.

Table 21.6. Punnett Square for eye color in Ned and Catelyn's offspring

	Ned's gametes	
	B	**b**
b	**Bb**	**bb**
b	**Bb**	**bb**

(Catelyn's gametes labels the rows)

For this cross, there is a 1:1 (or 50/50) ratio of the two genotypes. Half of the possible genotypes are **Bb**, and the other half of the possible genotypes are **bb**. Since **Bb** codes for dark eyes and **bb** codes for light eyes, there is also a 1:1 ratio of phenotypes.

Finally, let's apply this expected ratio of outcomes with the actual genotypes/phenotypes seen in Ned and Catelyn's offspring. Robb and Sansa have light eyes with a genotype of **bb**. Arya, Bran, and Rickon have dark eyes with a genotype of **Bb**. This fits with our analysis and what would be predicted by the Punnett Square.

 Exercise 21.4a: Single-character Punnett Square Analysis

Now you will perform another single-character analysis, this time for hair texture. Both Ned and Catelyn have wavy hair.

- What is Ned's genotype for hair texture? _____

- What types of gametes can he produce? _____

- What is Catelyn's genotype for hair texture? _____

- What types of gametes can she produce? _____

Complete the Punnett Square in Table 21.7 to determine the possible genotypes of Ned and Catelyn's children with respect to hair texture.

Table 21.7. Punnett Square for hair texture in Ned and Catelyn's offspring

Ned's gametes

Catelyn' s gametes

- How many genotypes are represented in the Punnett Square? _____

- Of the four possible outcomes in the Punnett Square, how many are **TT**? _____ And what phenotype would this genotype produce? _____

- Of the four possible outcomes in the Punnett Square, how many are **Tt**? _____ And what phenotype would this genotype produce? _____

- Of the four possible outcomes in the Punnett Square, how many are **tt**? _____ And what phenotype would this genotype produce? _____

Compare what you have found in this analysis with the actual phenotypes of the five children. Robb and Rickon have curly hair, Sansa has wavy hair, and Arya and Bran have straight hair.

- Does your Punnett Square predict that all three phenotypes are possible in Ned and Catelyn's offspring?

Activity 21.5: Two Character Analysis

Geneticists can also examine relatedness by considering two characteristics at the same time. A two-character analysis involves looking at the genotypes and phenotypes of two different gene loci. Examining multiple loci in the same analysis can give us a better understanding of overall relatedness.

Let's examine this using eye color and hair texture. Recall from Activity 21.2 that the eye color gene exhibits complete dominance while the hair texture gene exhibits incomplete dominance. We will use Robert and Jaime (from Exercise 21.2d) as our examples here. Robert has dark eyes and curly hair. For this example we will assume that Robert is heterozygous for eye color (**Bb**). So his two-character genotype would be **BbTT**.

 Exercise 21.5a: Two-character Analysis of a Family

Cersei has light eyes and wavy hair. Cersei has three children: Joffrey, Myrcella, and Tommen. Joffrey and Tommen have light eyes and straight hair, while Myrcella has light eyes and wavy hair just like her mother. Fill in Table 21.8 to reflect the genotypes of this family.

Table 21.8. Genotypes and Phenotypes of Cersei and her Family

Individual	Phenotype	Genotype
Jaime	Light eyes/Wavy hair	
Robert	Dark eyes/Curly hair	**BbTT**
Cersei	Light eyes/Wavy hair	
Joffrey	Light eyes/Straight hair	
Myrcella	Light eyes/Wavy hair	
Tommen	Light eyes/Straight hair	

Robert and Cersei are married, but there are a lot of rumors about whether or not Robert is actually the father of Cersei's three children. If the gossip is to be believed, Jaime is the actual father of Cersei's offspring. Geneticists (or you!) can figure out if the rumors are true based upon the genotypes of the children and their supposed parents.

Let's first examine the possible gametes that the parents can produce since those gametes are responsible for creating the children. We know that Robert's two-character genotype is **BbTT**. But we also know that the alleles for a gene locus separate during meiosis (this is explained by Mendel's Law of Segregation and Law of Independent Assortment). So the two alleles for eye color and the two alleles for hair texture will separate into two different gametes. The genotypes of the resulting gametes would be **BT** and **bT**. Note how each gamete only has one copy of each gene (because gametes are haploid). Fill in Table 21.9 to reflect the possible gametes of Jaime and Cersei.

Table 21.9. Genotypes of the Supposed Parents and Their Gametes

Individual	Genotype of the Diploid Individual	Genotypes of the Haploid Gametes
Jaime		
Robert	**BbTT**	**BT, bT**
Cersei		

Given this information we can determine if it's possible for Robert and/or Jaime to be the father of Cersei's offspring. Fill in Table 21.10 to reflect the genotypes of the children, Robert, and Cersei. For the last column, consider if any of the combinations of Robert's and Cersei's gametes could produce each child's genotype. If not, then Robert cannot be the father of that child.

Table 21.10. Evidence Regarding Robert's Possible Paternity

Individual	Genotype	Robert's Gametes	Cersei's Gametes	Can Robert be the Father?
Joffrey				
Myrcella				
Tommen				

Now fill in Table 21.11 to reflect the genotypes of the children, Robert, and Cersei. For the last column, consider if any of the combinations of Jaime's and Cersei's gametes could produce each child's genotype. If not, then Jaime cannot be the father of that child.

Table 21.11. Evidence Regarding Jaime's Possible Paternity

Individual	Genotype	Jaime's Gametes	Cersei's Gametes	Can Jaime be the Father?
Joffrey				
Myrcella				
Tommen				

- Given the evidence that you've gathered, who do you believe is the father of Cersei's children?

- Why? Explain how the combination of the parents' gametes could have produced all three children.

Pre-Lab Questions

1. Variations of genes are called _____.

2. If you are homozygous dominant for a trait, then that is your
   a. Genotype
   b. Phenotype
   c. Gametes

3. When a heterozygote produces gametes, the chance the dominant allele will be in a particular gamete is _____ percent.

4. In incomplete dominance, having one copy of the dominant allele means that you will produce the dominant phenotype.
   a. True
   b. False

Post-Lab Questions

1. If you see someone with dark eyes do you know his/her genotype? Explain.

2. Explain why the Punnett Square does not work for height in humans.

3. Jill has light eyes and her husband Jack has dark eyes. All of their ten children have dark eyes. What is Jack's genotype?

4. Sickle-cell anemia is a common disease in individuals from western Africa. An individual with the disease is homozygous for the mutated hemoglobin S allele (H^S). Heterozygotes and those homozygous for the normal hemoglobin A allele (H^A) show no symptoms. If two individuals who are both heterozygous for the condition have children, what percentage will have the disease? Show your Punnett square below.

5. Both Jill and Jack have brown eyes. Three of their ten children have blue eyes. What are Jill and Jack's genotypes? Show the Punnett square for them below.

6. Huntington's disease is a dominant trait that may not manifest itself until later in life. Jack's father has just been diagnosed with it. Could Jack be at risk of getting the disease?

7. Need more practice? Try these interactive websites.
   - https://public.biol.ksu.edu/genetics/story_html5.html
   - http://krupp.wcc.hawaii.edu/BIOL100/genetics/genetics1/GenProbl.htm

EL CENTRO CAMPUS BIOL 1406 PBL
Gel Electrophoresis

Goals

1. Explain how electrophoresis separates substances.
2. Identify the parts of the electrophoresis system and describe their functions.
3. Use the electrophoresis equipment to separate component dyes of a food color by size and/or charge.
4. Analyze the results of electrophoresis.

Activity 22.1: Gel Electrophoresis

Gel electrophoresis is a technique used to separate, identify, and analyze nucleic acids and proteins. This separation is based on the magnitude of charge as well as the size of a molecule. Because opposite charges attract, we can separate particles using an electrophoresis system, which consists of three basic components: a gel, a power supply, and a chamber.

A sample of what needs to be separated is loaded into the gel. The **gel** is the matrix in which the separation will occur and is composed of branched polysaccharides (Figure 21.1). The amount of branches determines how easy molecules move, based on their size. If the branching in the polysaccharide is numerous and frequent, only small molecules can pass through the spaces between the branches. If there are few branches, however, large molecules can pass through. Many of the gels used in electrophoresis contain the polysaccharide **agarose**, which is produced by certain seaweeds and is used in foods as a thickener.

Figure 22.1. Agarose gel

The **power supply** supplies electricity to the electrophoresis system (Figure 22.2). The electricity flows in one direction – from one end of the electrophoresis chamber to the other. The electrodes in the chamber, called the anode and the cathode, attract oppositely charged particles. If a molecule is strongly charged, it will quickly move toward the electrode of opposite charge. For example, a molecule that is negative will have an attraction to the positive electrode, while a positively charged molecule will be attracted to the negative electrode. However, size is also a factor when determining the rate of separation in electrophoresis. If two molecules possess the same magnitude of charge, the smaller molecule will migrate toward the electrode faster.

Figure 22.2. Power Supply

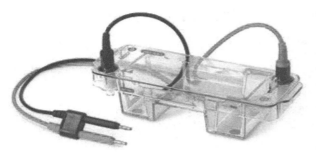

The electrophoresis **chamber** is basically a plastic container with the anode and cathode at opposite ends (Figure 22.3). A tray containing the gel is placed inside the chamber and a buffer is poured into the chamber until the gel is covered. The **buffer** is a solution that conducts electricity, allowing the electric current to flow from the cathode through the buffer to the anode.

Figure 22.3. Electrophoresis chamber

 Exercise 22.1a: Migration of Molecules

- Which would migrate faster using gel electrophoresis – a large uncharged molecule or a small negatively-charged molecule? Why?

 Exercise 22.1b: Anatomy of an Electrophoresis System

- Identify the different components of your electrophoresis system and describe the function of each component per Figure 4 and Table 1.

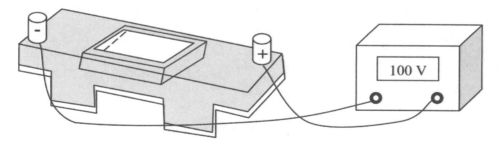

Figure 4. Electrophoresis System

Table 22.1. Parts and Functions of an Electrophoresis System

Part	Function
Agarose gel	Matrix through which the sample runs
Anode	Positive (red) electrode; negatively-charged particles migrate toward
Cathode	Negative (black) electrode; positively-charged particles migrate toward
Chamber	Supports gel and electrophoresis buffer
Electrophoresis buffer	Solution that conducts electrical current
Gel tray	Acts as a mold for agarose gel
Lid	Covers chamber & connects to power supply with electrical leads
Power supply	Provides electrical current to drive the migration of molecules

Exercise 22.1c: Using the Micropipette

Materials needed: gloves, micropipette, pipette tips, multi-well tray, food coloring or water for practice

1. Become familiar with the micropipette. Observe the control button, the volume adjustment knob (units in microliters, or µl), the tip ejector button, and the shaft. Refer to the diagram to the right.

2. Steps for using the micropipette:
   a. Hold the micropipette with thumb on the plunger and your fingers around the barrel.
   b. Attach a tip firmly on the end of the shaft.
   c. Gently depress the button to the first stop and place tip in liquid.
   d. Release the button slowly and draw up liquid all the way, keeping the tip in the liquid.
   e. Place tip against side of well or container to be pipetted and slowly push plunger to the second stop or all the way down. It may be helpful to guide or steady the shaft with your other hand. Do not release the plunger button until after the tip is removed from the container.

3. Adjusting the volume:
   a. Change the volume by rotating the dial just above the display. Within the display there are 3 digits with a red line that indicates a decimal point.
   b. These pipettes can be set from 1 to 20 microliters (µl). What is yours set to now?
   c. Practice using the pipette set at 10 µl - 15 µl.

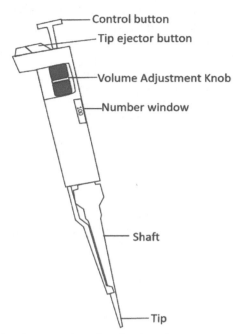

Control button
Tip ejector button
Volume Adjustment Knob
Number window
Shaft
Tip

 Exercise 22.1d: Running the Agarose Gel with Dyes

Materials needed: gloves, agarose gel, electrophoresis buffer, electrophoresis system, samples, micropipette, set of food coloring samples, small beaker for used tips

1. Examine your gel. The holes left by the teeth of the comb are called **wells**.
2. Place the gel tray in the gel box with the wells at the upper end.
3. Add enough electrophoresis buffer to the gel box to cover the gel with about 2 mm of buffer (must cover the wells).
4. Slowly and carefully transfer **10 µl** of one of the food dye mixtures into one of the wells. Repeat with the other dyes.
5. Place the lid on the chamber - be sure to orient the ends correctly. Plug in the leads to the power supply (**red to red and black to black**) and turn on the power supply to **100 volts**.
6. Press the **Run** button.
7. Look at the gel from time to time to see how the dyes are separating from one another. Notice how each dye moves in a straight line from its well towards the positive electrode. Thus, each dye stays in its own lane. Note which dyes move faster.
8. Once the fastest dye moves about two thirds of the way through the gel, turn off the power supply and remove the gel tray from the gel box.
9. Draw a picture of the separated dyes on the template in Post-Lab Question #1. Each lane contains all of the different color molecules found in one food color.
10. Use what you've learned about how gel electrophoresis separates molecules to determine the relative sizes of the dye molecules.

BIOL 1406 – Gel Electrophoresis Questions

Pre-Lab Questions

1. Electrophoresis separates particles based on charge and _____.
   a. size
   b. solubility
   c. color

2. The sample that needs to be separated is loaded into the
   a. power supply.
   b. electrophoresis chamber.
   c. gel.

3. The buffer solution allows the _____ to flow from one electrode to the other.

4. A negatively-charged molecule should migrate to the positive electrode.
   a. True
   b. False

Post-Lab Questions

1. Draw your electrophoresis results on this diagram:

2. Why is gel electrophoresis used?

3. What are some factors that affect the distance which molecules move though the gel?

4. What components are necessary to conduct gel electrophoresis?

5. Based on the migration of the dyes, what charge do the dyes have?

6. Which electrode should DNA (which is a negatively charged molecule) migrate toward in a gel electrophoresis system – the cathode or the anode? Why?

7. What would be the result if you used a gel that was denser than the agarose gel you used in this activity?

Goals

1. Explain why hemoglobin is an important molecule in red blood cells.
2. Explore the consequences of mutations in relation to hemoglobin.
3. Use the electrophoresis equipment to separate different types of hemoglobin.
4. Compare and evaluate the results of proteins separated by electrophoresis.

Activity 23.1: Sickle Cell Disorder

A molecule called **hemoglobin** is responsible for gas exchange in almost all vertebrates (animals with backbones) and even some invertebrates (animals without backbones). In vertebrates, hemoglobin is found within red blood cells, which travel through the circulatory system to deliver oxygen to tissues and rid the body of carbon dioxide. In respiratory organs such as lungs, oxygen diffuses from the lungs into the bloodstream where it binds to the hemoglobin in red blood cells. The red blood cells then make their way through branching blood vessels, eventually ending up in narrow capillaries that invade tissues. As cells require oxygen to undergo aerobic respiration, the cells found in most tissues require hemoglobin-packed red blood cells to deliver a constant supply of oxygen. Normal red blood cells have a biconcave shape (almost flat in the middle, but round on the edges) that allows them to flow freely through blood vessels and gives them the flexibility to squeeze through small capillaries.

Sickle cell disease (SCD) describes a group of inherited blood disorders, resulting in abnormal hemoglobin referred to as **hemoglobin S** or sickle hemoglobin. Under certain conditions, the sickle hemoglobin molecules bind together, distorting the cell to produce a crescent-shape, hence the term "sickle cell". The distorted cells are not flexible and can stick to the walls of blood vessels, causing a blockage that slows or stops the flow of blood. This results in pain and damage to oxygen-deprived organs. In addition, the distorted red blood cells are destroyed by the body at a high rate, resulting in low levels of red blood cells (i.e. anemia).

Hemoglobin S is due to a **mutation**, a change in the nucleotide sequence of a gene, of the β-globin gene on chromosome 11. Hemoglobin consists of two β-globin and two α-globin subunits. In many cases, this mutation is caused by the substitution of a nucleotide, resulting in the translation of a protein subunit with valine as the sixth amino acid instead of glutamate (also called glutamic acid). Normal hemoglobin, **hemoglobin A**, does not bind together due to the nature of glutamate's R group. However, valine has a nonpolar subgroup, which accounts for the tendency for hemoglobin S to bind together into long rods.

Each person has two alleles for the β-globin gene. People who inherit one mutated form of the allele and one normal allele have sickle cell trait (SCT). People with SCT usually show no symptoms of SCD, as roughly half of their hemoglobin is normal. However, those with SCT can pass the abnormal allele to their children. People who have SCD inherit two abnormal hemoglobin alleles, one from each parent.

Exercise 23.1a: Genes and Expression   *Lecture*

Using **H^A** and **H^S** write the allele pair for the following β-globin genotypes, as well as the corresponding phenotype.

	Allele pair for genotype	Phenotype
Homozygous		
Heterozygous		
Homozygous		

- Does this gene locus exhibit complete, incomplete, or co-dominance?

 Exercise 23.1b: Sickle Cell Disease and Heredity   *Lecture*

A man who is heterozygous for the sickle cell trait has a child with a woman who is also heterozygous. What is the percent likelihood that their child will be homozygous recessive and carry two hemoglobin S alleles?

✋ **Exercise 23.1c: Who's Faster – Glutamate or Valine?**

As β-globin is part of hemoglobin it can be used to determine what alleles an individual possesses. There is only one difference between the normal and sickle form of hemoglobin – the amino acid in the sixth position of the β-globin chain. The normal β-globin has <u>glutamate</u> in the sixth position, a negatively-charged amino acid, while the sickle form of β-globin has <u>valine</u>, a nonpolar amino acid.

- The first seven amino acids in normal β-globin are:

    Valine-Histidine-Leucine-Threonine-Proline-Glutamate-Glutamate...

- Thus, the first seven amino acids of sickle β-globin are (fill in the seven amino acid sequence below):

Activity 23.2: Comets and Hemoglobin

Dr. Luna Tic, a world-renowned expert in astrophysics and pet grooming, has issued a dire warning that the next comet to pass Earth will produce a series of catastrophic events. One of the most alarming is the comet's effect on the human race. Dr. Tic hypothesizes the radiation emitted by the comet will result in transformations of epic proportions based on a person's genotype at the β-globin locus.

She predicts the following transformations based on genotype:
- *Homozygous normal = Zombie*
- *Heterozygous = Werewolf*
- *Homozygous sickle = Vampire*

Your friends Maggie and Glen, who are expecting twins, would like to find out what they will transform into once the comet passes. Since you are a biologist, they know you can figure this out. Blood samples have been taken from Maggie and Glen and the hemoglobin has been isolated, but you must now run an electrophoresis gel to discover their genotypes.

 Exercise 23.2a: Preparing and Running the Gel

Materials needed: goggles, gloves, agarose gel in tray, electrophoresis buffer, electrophoresis chamber, power supply, micropipette and tips, Quickstrips Hemoglobin samples.

1. Wearing gloves, place the tray with gel into the chamber so that the wells are at the **black electrode end**.
2. Fill the chamber with electrophoresis buffer until the wells are well covered or to the fill level marked on the outside of the chamber.
3. Set the micropipette to **15 μl**.
4. Tap the foil top of the Quickstrip so samples fall to the bottom of the tubes. Since the samples are vacuum sealed, some samples may not fall.
5. Pierce the foil of tube A with the tip of the micropipette.
6. Load sample A into the first well. Do the same with the remaining samples.
   a. Load the wells in consecutive order. Examine diagram in Exercise 2c to make sure you load the samples correctly.
   b. **Make sure you change tips each time you load a new sample.**
7. Attach the lid to the chamber and plug the wires into the power supply, **red to red and black to black**.
8. Check to be sure the gel is oriented in the correct direction.
9. Start running the gel:
   a. Turn on the power supply at the toggle switch
   b. Turn the Voltage to **125**V
   c. Press the **Run/Pause button** to start.
10. Run for 20 minutes. If it is running, you will see lots of bubbles at the head of the gel as the current passes through the system.

Many different types of molecules can be separated using electrophoresis. We can use enzymes to cut DNA into fragments, which are then separated by electrophoresis and analyzed based on the different sizes to diagnose a deadly disease or determine if the sample came from the suspect in a murder, for instance. Proteins can also be separated using electrophoresis.

Your sample will run to the positively-charged end of the electrophoresis chamber. Considering the properties of glutamate and valine's R groups, *which sample should migrate faster and why*?

 Exercise 23.2c: Analyzing the Results

1. After 20 minutes, press the **Run/Pause button.**
2. Observe the gel and on the diagram below, copy the bands you see for each lane.
3. The samples in each lane are as folows:

>   A – Normal Hemoglobin control
>   B – Sickle Hemoglobin control
>   C – Carrier Hemoglobin control
>   D – Maggie's Hemoglobin
>   E – Glen's Hemoglobin

4. Using the controls, determine Maggie and Glen's genotypes.

Pre-Lab Questions

1. Sickle cell disease affects which protein in the blood?
    a. Hemoglobin
    b. Collagen
    c. Fibrin

2. A mutation is the change in the nucleotide sequence of a gene.
    a. True
    b. False

3. If a person exhibits the SCT phenotype, which genotype would the person have?
    a. H^AH^A
    b. H^AH^S
    c. H^SH^S

4. Hemoglobin is a protein made up of which two different subunits?

    _____

Post-Lab Questions

1. Why is a mutation in the protein subunit globin important to the function of hemoglobin?

2. Were you correct about which hemoglobin would migrate faster? Why or why not?

3. Why is it important to position the hemoglobin samples near the negative electrode?

4. Based on their genotypes, what will Maggie and Glen transform into once the comet passes Earth? (Assuming that Dr. Luna Tic's hypothesis is correct!) How did the electrophoresis results help you come to this conclusion?

5. Maggie is pregnant with fraternal (non-identical) twins. Given Maggie and Glen's genotypes, what is the probability that their children will become zombies? Werewolves? Vampires?

EL CENTRO CAMPUS BIOL 1406 PBL
Gene Expression

Goals

1. Identify the components of RNA nucleotides.
2. Explain the differences between DNA and RNA.
3. Demonstrate the DNA transcription and translation processes.
4. Identify the types and functions of RNA molecules.
5. Define codon and anticodon.
6. Explain how a DNA nucleotide sequence becomes a protein amino acid sequence.

Activity 24.1: Ribonucleic Acid (RNA)

Although both are nucleic acids, DNA and RNA differ in several ways. As the names suggest, the pentose sugars in the nucleotides differ. In DNA nucleotides, the sugar component is deoxyribose, while it is ribose in RNA nucleotides (Figure 24.1). RNA also lacks the nitrogenous base thymine and instead uses uracil.

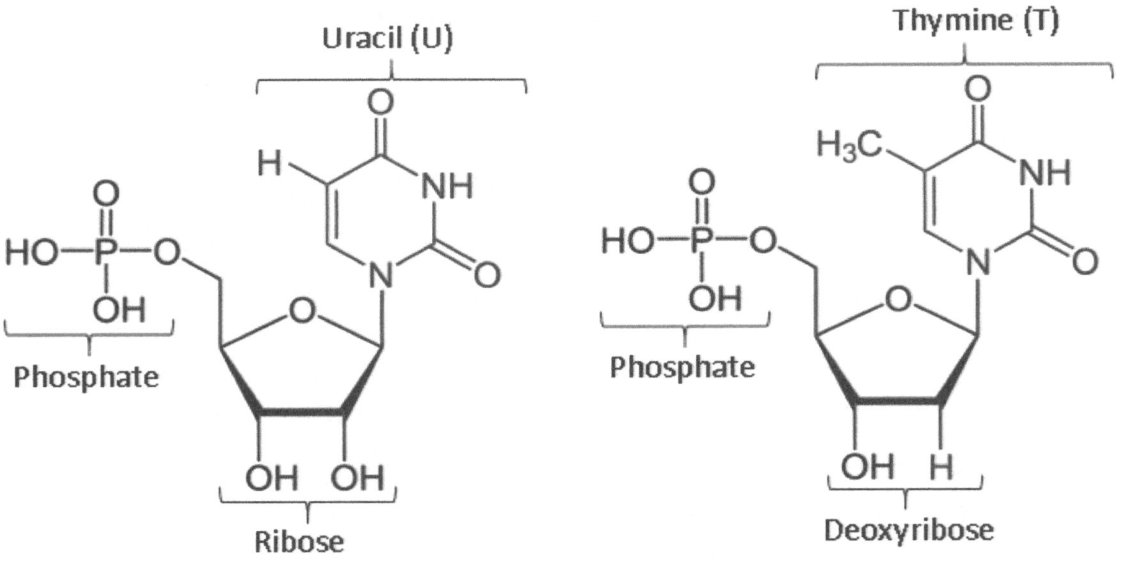

Figure 24.1. Uracil and Thymine Nucleotides

✏ **Exercise 24.1: Molecular Arrangement of RNA Nucleotides** *Lecture*

- Compare deoxyribose and ribose components. What are the differences?

- Compare the uracil base to the thymine base. What are the structural differences?

Activity 24.2: Transcription and Translation

Gene expression is a process in which the information in a gene is used to synthesize a product. Depending of the gene that is expressed, the final product may be RNA or protein. Synthesis of RNA is accomplished by transcription, while **protein synthesis** begins with transcription and ends with translation.

Transcription produces a strand of RNA nucleotides using DNA as a template. This process may result in the production of an RNA molecule that regulates gene expression, such as microRNA (miRNA). Other types of RNA are directly involved in protein synthesis, like transfer RNA (tRNA) and ribosomal RNA (rRNA). If the gene contains the recipe for a protein then transcription will result in the synthesis of messenger RNA. **Messenger RNA** (mRNA) carries the information of the gene in its RNA nucleotide sequence, which will be decoded during translation to produce a polypeptide. (The term **polypeptide** is used when a protein is initially built, as the original amino acid sequence is typically modified in the final protein.) For example, Figure 24.2 shows a segment of DNA containing a small gene and the mRNA that would be transcribed from that gene. In reality, mRNA is typically thousands of nucleotides long.

3'-TACGTACTCGGGAGCCGGACT-5'
5'-ATGCATGAGCCCTCGGCCTGA-3'

5'-AUGCAUGAGCCCUCGGCCUGA-3'

Figure 24.2. Double-stranded DNA (top) and mRNA (bottom)

Translation is the synthesis of a polypeptide using the information encoded in the nucleotide sequence of the mRNA. The information in the mRNA is arranged in **codons**, which are groups of three nucleotides that correspond to specific amino acids. For example, the first portion of the mRNA sequence in Figure 24.2 is 5'-AUGCAUGAG-3' and contains three codons: AUG is the first codon, CAU is the second codon, and GAG is the third codon. Translation occurs at a ribosome, which binds the mRNA. According to the sequence of the codons in the mRNA, tRNAs bring the corresponding amino acids and the ribosome forms a peptide bond between each amino acid. Translation will stop at a specific codon called a **stop codon**.

 Exercise 24.2: DNA and mRNA   *Lecture*

- Examine both strands in the double-stranded DNA in Figure 24.2. Which strand is the template for the mRNA – the upper or lower? Why?

- How many codons are in the mRNA? How many amino acids should be translated from the mRNA?

Activity 24.2: DNA Transcription

The synthesis of protein from the DNA instructions in a gene is a multistep process. First the DNA must be transcribed into RNA. (specifically messenger RNA (mRNA)) Then the nucleotide sequence from RNA is translated (or decoded) into the amino acid sequence of a protein. Transcription is similar to DNA replication, but it has some significant differences. Instead of using DNA polymerase, an **RNA polymerase** builds the RNA strand. Only one strand (the template strand) of the DNA is transcribed. Like DNA synthesis RNA nucleotides are only added to the 3' end of the growing mRNA molecule. The DNA template strand is thus read 3' to 5' but the mRNA is built antiparallel to the template strand in a 5' to 3' direction. After the mRNA transcript is created it is modified before exiting the nucleus.

 Exercise 24.2: Transcribing from the template strand

Each lab group will be assigned one DNA template strand to transcribe. It is important to remember the DNA is double stranded, but you are only concerned about the template strand for transcription. Also, the mRNA is synthesized by RNA polymerase in a 5' to 3' direction, antiparallel to the template strand.

DNA template strand:

1.   3' GGG-TAC-GGC-TCT-TCG-GGA-ATC-TTT 5'

2.   3' GGG-TAC-GGC-CTT-ACC-ACG-ATC-TTT 5'

- Circle the template strand you were assigned.

Use the template strand to transcribe your mRNA molecule.

- How many codons are in your mRNA molecule?

Checkpoint A

Activity 24.3: DNA Translation

Ribonucleic acid (RNA) has many important functions in the cell. While DNA molecules contain all of an organism's hereditary information, RNA is essential in the formation of the final product, usually a protein. Three different types of RNA are necessary for protein synthesis: messenger RNA, ribosomal RNA, and transfer RNA.

Messenger RNA (mRNA) can be thousands of nucleotides long and it carries the sequence that will be "decoded" to produce a protein. The mRNA nucleotide sequence is "read" in three-nucleotide sections called **codons**. For example, an RNA sequence 5'-AUGCAUGAG-3' is three codons long -

AUG is the first codon, CAU is the second codon and GAG is the last codon. Table 24.1 lists the mRNA codons and the amino acids that they code for. Our sequence would translate into the amino acid sequence Methionine – Histidine – Glutamic acid. Notice that several codons can code for the same amino acid. Three of the codons are STOP codons; when they are reached, protein synthesis ends. This occurs because a protein called a release factor binds to the stop codon and triggers the release of the polypeptide chain.

Table 24.1. The Genetic Code

mRNA codon	Amino Acid Specified	mRNA codon	Amino Acid Specified	mRNA codon	Amino Acid Specified	mRNA codon	Amino Acid Specified
AAU	Asparagine	CAU	Histidine	GAU	Aspartic acid	UAU	Tyrosine
AAC		CAC		GAC		UAC	
AAA	Lysine	CAA	Glutamine	GAA	Glutamic acid	UAA	STOP
AAG		CAG		GAG		UAG	STOP
ACU	Threonine	CCU	Proline	GCU	Alanine	UCU	Serine
ACC		CCC		GCC		UCC	
ACA		CCA		GCA		UCA	
ACG		CCG		GCG		UCG	
AGU	Serine	CGU	Arginine	GGU	Glycine	UGU	Cysteine
AGC		CGC		GGC		UGC	
AGA	Arginine	CGA		GGA		UGA	STOP
AGG		CGG		GGG		UGG	Tryptophan
AUU	Isoleucine	CUU	Leucine	GUU	Valine	UUU	Phenylalanine
AUC		CUC		GUC		UUC	
AUA		CUA		GUA		UUA	Leucine
AUG	Methionine	CUG		GUG		UUG	

Ribosomal RNA (rRNA) can vary from around 100 to over 4,000 nucleotides. They are an integral part of the enzymes that catalyze the translation process. Because these enzymes are unique in containing both proteins and RNA, they are referred to as **ribosomes**. Ribosomes are produced in the nucleolus of the nucleus.

Transfer RNAs (tRNA) are small segments of RNA around 80 nucleotides in length. They function as the "decoder key" during translation. Each one binds to a specific amino acid and transports the amino acid to the ribosome. A particular region on the tRNA called the **anticodon** has a unique 3 nucleotide sequence (Figure 24.2). The anticodon corresponds with a codon on an mRNA molecule. For example, the anti-codon for the AUG codon is UAC. This tRNA carries the amino acid methionine. For each codon there is an anti-codon that will pair with it - except for the three stop codons.

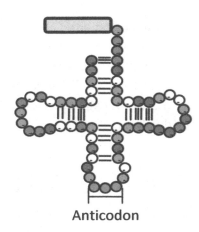

Anticodon

Figure 24.2. Generalized two-dimensional structure of a tRNA molecule. The red nucleotides are the anti-codon nucleotides that correspond with the codon on the mRNA molecule.

 Exercise 24.3: Transfer RNA

Answer the questions below about the following mRNA codon: AAG

- What amino acid would the tRNA that corresponds to this codon carry?

- Will this tRNA molecule ever carry a different amino acid?

- What anticodon would the tRNA have to bind to this codon?

- How many other tRNAs will carry the same amino acid as this tRNA?

Activity 24.4: Translation – Protein Synthesis

Translation is the final step in producing a protein from the DNA instructions in a gene. In addition to the mRNA, a ribosome and many transfer RNAs are required to build a protein. In prokaryotes, transcription and translation occur simultaneously, as no nucleus separates the two processes. In eukaryotes, translation occurs at free ribosomes floating in the cytosol of the cell or at bound ribosomes on the rough endoplasmic reticulum. As shown in Figure 24.3, ribosomes are composed of two subunits aptly named the large and small subunit, which only come together during translation. The initiation of translation begins with the mRNA binding to the small subunit of the ribosome. Next, a methionine tRNA molecule binds to the AUG start codon on an mRNA molecule. When this is all in place, the large subunit of the ribosome binds to the complex with the tRNA in its P-site. The large subunit of the ribosome contains three sites where tRNAs can be located – the **P-site** (P for Peptidyl-tRNA binding site, as a peptide bond is formed in the site) and the **A-site** (A for Aminoacyl tRNA binding site, as this is the full name for the tRNA molecules that have been "charged" with an amino acid). A tRNA that corresponds to the next mRNA codon will bind to the A-site of the ribosome. The ribosome then catalyzes the peptide bond by adding the polypeptide from the tRNA in the P-site to the newcomer tRNA in the A-site. After transferring its polypeptide, the first tRNA is moved to the **E-site** (E for Exit) and released. The ribosome moves down the mRNA molecule so that the second tRNA is moved to the P-site. The growing polypeptide extends from the ribosome through the exit tunnel. This process repeats until a STOP codon reaches the A site.

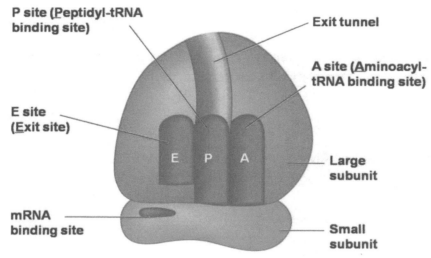

Figure 24.3. Anatomy of a Ribosome

✋ **Exercise 24.4: Translating the m-RNA molecule**

Table 24.2. The Base Pair Decoder

Codon	Word represented
AGA	THE
UUU	LIFE
GAA	ALL
UAG	STOP (.)
UGC	YOU
CCC	ERINACEOUS
CCU	SUBJECT
UUA	DNA
AUG	BIOLOGY
UUG	FOR
CCG	IS
AGC	BEST
UGG	AROUND
UUC	CODE
AAA	PURPLE

1. Using the mRNA molecule you transcribed in Exercise 24.2, you will translate your codons to words to form a sentence. Each word in your sentence represents a specific amino acid. Each complete sentence represents a complete protein. Rewrite the mRNA from Exercise 24.2:

- Translate mRNA using the Table 24.2 decoder:

- Does the sentence make sense? If not, what error(s) did you make during transcription and/or translation? Be sure to fix them before moving on to #2.

2. Now that you know your mRNA is correct, use the genetic code information from Table 24.1 to translate your mRNA to the proper **amino acid** sequence.

3. How many amino acids are in the completed protein? Does this number match the number of codons in your mRNA molecule? Why or why not?

4. Consider the following mRNA codon sequence: AUGCC<u>C</u>CCGGAAUGGUGCUAG. If an error occurred during transcription, and the sequence was changed to AUGCC<u>A</u>CCGGAAUGGUGCUAG, how would the resulting polypeptide be affected? What type of point mutation is this?

5. What if the sequence was changed from AUG<u>C</u>CCCCGGAAUGAUGCUAG to AUG<u>A</u>CCCCGGAAUGAUGCUAG? How would the resulting polypeptide be affected? What type of point mutation is this?

BIOL 1406 – Gene Expression Questions
Pre-Lab Questions

1. _____ and translation are the two processes that occur in protein expression.

2. Which nucleotide is found in RNA, but not DNA?
   a. Adenine
   b. Guanine
   c. Uracil

3. What is the product of transcription?
   a. Protein
   b. mRNA
   c. DNA

4. Where is the site of translation?

   _____

Post-Lab Questions

1. What are the base pairing rules for RNA?

2. How does DNA transcription differ from DNA replication?

3. What are the types of RNA necessary for translation and how do they work together?

4. Which RNA molecules have codons and which have anticodons?

5. What steps are necessary for the DNA sequence 3'-TACGTCTAGCATATC-5' to become a protein? What amino acid sequence is produced?

6. What would be the outcome if a mutation occurred so that the above sequence was changed to 3'-TACATCTAGCATATC-5' ? What type of mutation is this?

7. What would be the outcome if a mutation occurred so that the above sequence was changed to 3'-TACGTCTATCATATC-5' ? What type of mutation is this?

8. Give a possible 3' to 5' sequence of a **DNA** molecule that would code for a polypeptide with the amino acid sequence of Methionine – Tryptophan – Histidine – Lysine.

Goals
1. Define epigenetics.
2. Watch "Ghosts in Your Genes" video about epigenetics.
3. Explain the significance of experiments on epigenetics.

Activity 24.1: Epigenetics

Each somatic cell in a human body contains the same 46 chromosomes as every other cell, however they are not all alike. Nerve cells are long and thin and specially adapted for transmitting signals, whereas skin cells are small and flat and connected to other skin cells to create a barrier. These differences arise because of epigenetics. **Epigenetics** is the regulation of genes, which ones are turned on and which ones are turned off. Another good example is the production of lactase, the enzyme that breaks down lactose (milk sugar). Virtually all humans have the ability to produce lactase as infants. Some humans turn off the gene to produce the enzyme and others continue to produce the enzyme throughout their adult life. Adults without the ability to produce the enzyme are lactose intolerant. ow your cells regulate the transcription of genes is an exciting field of study.

 Exercise 25.1: "Ghosts in Your Genes" Video

Answer the following questions while watching the video.

- How many genes are in the human genome?

- What is the difference between Angelman Syndrome and Prader-WIlli Syndrome?

- What are the two ways in which genes can be turned on and off?

- What is the genetic difference between the skinny brown mice and the fat yellow mice?

- How did feeding folic acid to pregnant fat yellow mice affect their offspring? And why were the results of the experiment so important?

- What were the findings of the experiment comparing gene expression in identical twins of various ages?

- What were the findings of the experiment that compared the effects of maternal care in rats on offspring behavior?

- What is the evidence that early experience in humans can affect our health?

- Do the results of the experiment on humans with M.D.S. leukemia support the hypothesis that this cancer can be treated by changing gene expression?

- What evidence is there that autism may have an epigenetic trigger?

- What did the research in the Swedish village find out about diet and life expectancy in future generations?

- What were the conclusions of the study on the effect of pesticide exposure in pregnant rats?